Rainbow Unzipped

First published in 2009
by HEADLINE PUBLISHING GROUP

Cataloguing in Publication Data is available from the British Library

ISBN 978 0 7553 1976 3

Design by Jim Lockwood

Printed and bound in Great Britain by Butler Tanner and Dennis Ltd, Frome, Somerset

Headline's policy is to use papers that are natural, renewable and recyclable products and made from wood grown in sustainable forests. The logging and manufacturing processes are expected to conform to the environmental regulations of the country of origin.

HEADLINE PUBLISHING GROUP
An Hachette UK Company
338 Euston Road
London NW1 3BH

www.headline.co.uk
www.hachette.co.uk

Contents

Foreword

Hello everybody!

Welcome to our autobiography. After 20 years of Geoffrey telling us stories, we thought it was about time we told you ours. We do hope you like it.

Being on *Rainbow* was a rollercoaster ride for all of us. A furry, multicoloured and extraordinary journey that was to lead to fame, fortune and fabulousness beyond our wildest dreams.

In this autobiography we want to share with you, our lovely fans, the highs and lows of our lives behind the scenes on *Rainbow* and beyond; we will reveal never before published stories and, where necessary, set the record straight.

Revisiting the past has been emotional to say the least and the three of us do hope you aren't too shocked by the revelations inside...

Happy reading!

Zippy   George   Bungle

THE RAINBOW
FRIENDS!

BY...
Jack

Future's so bright
we gotta wear shades!

by Grace

rainbow forever

I ♥ RBW

All the Gang, 1983

rainbow

Prologue

It had been seventeen years since Zippy, George and Bungle were all in the same room together and that was when they'd filmed the emotionally wrought final ever episode of *Rainbow*. A traumatic day that had ended in tears, recriminations and a bucket-load of bear barf unexpectedly cascading into Geoffrey's lap.

Yet here they were again, backstage at the Royal Festival Hall in London where the trio were only moments away from accepting a Lifetime Achievement Award for their services to children's television. A reunion possibly more stressful than those of the Spice Girls, Blur and Spandau Ballet combined.

Amazingly, after several hours together in the same building, as yet there hadn't been a cross word, no one had fallen off the wagon, nor had anyone attempted to lock themselves in their dressing room and refuse to come out. This, however, was largely due to the fact that neither George, Zippy nor Bungle were actually speaking to each other.

Standing to one side on his own, Zippy was in reflective mode as he slurped a glass of vintage Vimto and watched a nervous-looking Bungle pace up and down by the emergency exit, as if he was about to make a run for it at any moment.

'Five minutes please, guys,' announced the stage manager, before muttering something into her headpiece about being able to cut the atmosphere with a knife. 'They clearly hate each other,' she whispered gleefully.

Meanwhile, George was in front of the mirror being fussed over by his Japanese stylist Mee-Ow and Brad, his personal make-up artist, a tight T-shirted Zac Efron lookalike who seemed to be permanently at George's side whether he needed his make-up doing or not.

At that moment George spotted Zippy looking across at him. Their eyes locked and, for a split second, George considered smiling back. Wasn't it time to let bygones be bygones? After all, their big fall-out had been so long ago. And maybe Zippy wasn't looking quite so pleased with himself as he did in the old days. Then again, it was always hard to tell what his former on-screen partner was thinking – that metalled mouth had never been the most expressive of orifices.

It took the bigger person to make the first move, George thought to himself. Taking a deep breath, he was about to lift his furry mitt and wave at Zippy when Mee-Ow blocked his view, brandishing quite the most fabulous sequinned feather boa he'd ever seen, and suddenly, as quick as it'd come, the moment was gone.

> **Zippy couldn't face a scene – he'd predict when that bum-fluffed hippo was about to throw another hissy fit**

Coincidentally, Zippy had also been thinking about acknowledging George. Maybe not with a wave. But perhaps a nod of the head was what the situation called for. They'd be on stage within minutes pretending to be bosom buddies, so why not just break the ice now? On the other hand (not that he had one), Zippy couldn't face a scene – he'd never been able to predict when that bum-fluffed hippo was about to throw another hissy fit.

As they prepared for their comeback, older and wiser, the former *Rainbow* stars found themselves contemplating how it had all begun and just how they'd ended up not as the best of furry friends, but the bitterest of enemies...

CHAPTER 1
BUNGLED BEGINNINGS

Up above the streets and houses a rainbow was flying high – everyone could see it smiling over the sky. But for three wide-eyed youngsters, little did they know that the rainbows that entranced them through childhood would also be the name of the TV show that was to make them and perhaps – for one of them at least – break them. But that was a

Baby George weeps after being found abandoned at the Odeon Southend-on-Sea

RIGHT: A star is born? George puts a smile on matron's face at the orphanage

long time in the future. For now, rainbows came to play a part in each of their young lives, and whilst their experiences of this multicoloured archway may have all been very different, they all had one thing in common. Their rainbows offered hope.

The first time George saw a rainbow was the day he met his mum and dad. Although he always refers to them as his real parents – after all, they were the ones who had brought him up – George was in fact adopted, having been discovered by an usherette's flashlight halfway through a showing of *A Streetcar Named Desire* at the Odeon, Southend-on-Sea. Perhaps that spotlit moment cemented his destiny to perform. Wrapped in only a puce feather boa and still clutching a handful of popcorn he was immediately taken to the orphanage.

But Jean wasn't listening. She'd seen a little boy, pastel-coloured, furry. Or was it a hippo? She couldn't tell and didn't care

When Bob and Jean Simcock gingerly stepped into the chaotic playroom, their hearts felt ready to explode. All around them were children – rolling around on the floor with their toys, smearing jam on the walls or engrossed in their colouring books. They were all orphans looking to be loved and at that moment Jean wanted to scoop the lot of them up and take them back to the empty nursery in their home in the Kent countryside. Unable to have children of their own, the young couple had decided to adopt.

'What about that one over there?' said Bob, pointing at a tubby red-faced little girl with two fingers stuffed up her nostrils.

But Jean wasn't listening. She'd seen a little boy, pastel-coloured, furry. Or was it a hippo? She couldn't tell and didn't care. Because whatever this creature in the corner quietly playing on his own with a battered Tiny Tears was, Jean was smitten. He was the cutest little pink fluffy thing she'd ever seen.

'Isn't he adorable?' she whispered breathlessly to Bob. At that moment, as if he felt their eyes on him, the pink bundle turned and looked at the adoring couple. And when his big loveable blue eyes, complete with ready-curled eyelashes, locked into Jean's she knew here was the answer, no, the reason for all the heartache they'd suffered when her body had repeatedly refused to allow them their dream. All the anger and hurt she'd felt simply melted away when this child looked into her eyes. Now, at last, they were going to be a family.

Jean knelt down beside him. 'Hello there,' she said softly. 'My name's Jean, this is my husband Bob. What's yours?' she asked.

'George,' came the shy reply.

He paused, unsure for a second, his eyes taking in the smiling couple. And Bob never failed to delight in telling the story of how at the very moment little George was deciding whether to trust them, a huge rainbow broke through the clouds in the window behind them, forming what looked like a shining halo around George's furry head.

'Our own pink angel,' Jean whispered, clutching her heart and scarcely holding back the tears.

Then, picking up a tatty copy of *Jackie* magazine from the floor George offered it up to his potential parents. 'Can I have a story please, Jean?' he asked. Who knew back then that the first question he asked his parents would become the catchphrase that would catapult him to fame and make George one of the most recognisable pink hippo-type things in the country?

From that moment on, the family unit became inseparable. However, while little orphan George was growing up loved and wanted in leafy middle-class Kent, it was a very different story for Zippy.

For him, childhood meant freezing his knobbly backside off

in a dank two-up, two-down in the backstreets of a little-known mining town named Macclechester. Perhaps the one thing he had in common with George was that he never knew his real mum. He was brought up by his stepmother; a stern, steely (and latterly incontinent) woman, whose only pleasure in life seemed to be belittling Zippy and his brother and sister.

If Zippy or his siblings ever stepped out of line she'd either stick their heads in a bucket of cold water until their zips rusted or just padlock them closed. And they were poor. In fact, they were so poor Zippy once made a hole in the kitchen wall, behind the cooker, in order to dip his bread in next door's gravy.

The story went that Zippy's mother had run off with a one-

BELOW: The bad old days. A rare childhood photograph of Zippy (left) with his dad and younger sister Zoozie

armed hispanic juggler she'd met when the circus came to town. Zippy remembered her with fondness – the sweet smell of candy floss on her boozy blouse, her lone tooth and dark moustache. His step mum often said Zippy took after her, but by the way she curled her lip and spat out the words when she spoke this, he never felt able to take it as a compliment.

Meanwhile, Zippy's dad was a distant figure, either down t'pit or down t'pub, and they had little in common, other than the way their zips both hung to the right. While his dad seemed happy with the drudgery of small town life, even as a child, Zippy had aspirations. He just wanted more than this – so much more.

In fact, they were so poor Zippy once made a hole in the kitchen wall, behind the cooker, in order to dip his bread in next door's gravy

From a young age, Zippy had to get used to living without love. But one thing he vowed to himself was that he was not going to get used to living without money. On his way home from school he'd hang around the rich kids' houses and stare at their television sets through the windows. Sometimes he'd watch shiny new Morris Minors hurrying through the neighbourhood and he felt their sense of urgency. They wanted to get the hell out of there before any of the surrounding working-class grubbiness could rub off on them. Zippy knew how they felt.

In his longing for a better life, he was often caught standing at the side of the road being sprayed with muddy puddle water as the cars sped by. The rich kids pulled faces and laughed at him through the rear window. He'd respond by sticking two fingers up at them. He wasn't being rude, two fingers was all he had. 'It's not fair,' he muttered to himself. 'But one day I'm going to be richer than any of you.' He turned around when he heard mocking laughter behind him. It was his stepmother: 'Listen, you'll amount to nowt just like yer mam. You mark my words. Now, get out back and give that lav a good scrubbing,' she snapped, clipping him roughly around the head with a rag. 'Yer father left his mark on the rim last night and it's making me heave...'

Time passed, but while the other kids played footy and hopscotch on the cobbles, Zippy would sit on his doorstep daydreaming. There had to be another life out there. A better life. Occasionally, it would actually stop raining in Macclechester for a minute and a rainbow would form in the sky. Somehow Zippy felt spurred on by this break in the clouds. He convinced himself it was a sign. He'd heard about the pot of gold at the end of the rainbow and thought it deeply romantic. He just had to work out a way to get there.

Perhaps it was Bungle whose life was to unravel most unexpectedly. Who would have thought that someone who had spent their formative years generally doing what bears do in the woods, would end up becoming a household name? Looking back, a melancholic Bungle has often admitted how he lost the ability to see the wood for the trees once he found fame and how, ironically, being alone in the wilderness only became a reality when he moved to the bright lights of the city.

It was while romping around as nature intended at his home in the New Forest, that Bungle was spotted by a hemp-wearing theatre producer on a rambling holiday with his family. After a hugely successful and groundbreaking all-male version of *Annie Get Your Gun*, he was casting an all-bear production of *The Wizard Of Oz*. And as soon as he saw Bungle devouring a dead rabbit he turned to his barefoot wife, and excitedly said: 'Think "bow in his hair". Darling Moonshadow, I think we've found our Toto!'

Whilst the show itself received mixed reviews from the critics ('Un-Bear-able!' said the *Daily Mail*), Bungle received universal praise for his pitch-perfect and confident performance. Being in a theatre felt magical to him and, every night without fail, when Dorothy Bear sang 'Over the Rainbow', young Bungle's bear-bumps would make his fur stand on end. It was as if Yip Harburg's lyrics were speaking directly to him. He felt a connection with the song and it made him realise that acting, performing and being in front of a crowd was where he belonged and he wanted to do it for the rest of his life.

When the show finally closed – after six months at the London Palladium – Bungle enrolled at the Dame Babs Granditer's Stage School in East Finchley and within a year had appeared in TV adverts for both toilet roll and hair removal cream.

By the time the auditions for *Rainbow* were advertised all three of them had started working their

He felt a connection with the song and it made him realize that acting, performing and being in front of a crowd was where he belonged and he wanted to do it for the rest of his life

way up the showbiz ladder. Bungle made the transition from child star to adult performer and was perhaps initially the most recognisable face in the cast thanks to his appearance as furry roadkill in a controversial new TV drink-driving campaign. George – who had enjoyed dressing up in Jean's twin-sets from an early age – had made something of a name for himself on the drag scene under the guise of Georgette Hippo'pottymouth and had even understudied for Danny La Rue when the legendary female impersonator broke a nail and was forced to miss a performance.

Meanwhile, Zippy couldn't pack his knapsack quick enough

OPPOSITE:
A hairy moment?
Fresh-faced Bungle
gets ahead in
advertising

Tonite!
MADAME DODO'S CABARET LOUNGE
BREWER STREET, SOHO

proudly presents live on stage

Miss Georgette Hippo'pottymouth

'She wants you to play with her Ding-A-Ling!'

**plus
Blindfolded
Bingo!**

ZIPPY
Contact: *Stardust Talent* **01-282-158**

ZIPPY
Contact: *Stardust Talent* **01-282-158**

when his chance to escape grimy mining town life arrived on the doormat – a letter informing him he'd won a scholarship to RADA. Once there he happily shed his northern accent within a week. After a year in rep at the Oxford Playhouse playing everything from Shakespeare to the back-end of a pantomime cow, he was now ready for the big time. And the big time, in those days, meant television.

The auditions were advertised in *The Stage* newspaper in July 1972: 'Wanted: Brightly coloured outgoing new faces for *Rainbow*, a brand new educational Thames Television children's series. Applicants must be pink, tan or brown and enjoy listening to stories. Strictly no grey applicants. Please all bring CV & photo and rehearse one song which demonstrates your personality (16 bars required – bring sheet music).'

ABOVE: Strike a pose! It's an actor's life for RADA trained Zippy
OPPOSITE: A young George makes a name for himself on the Soho drag scene

WANTED

Brightly coloured outgoing new faces for
'RAINBOW' - a brand new educational
Thames Television children's series.
Applicants must be pink, tan or brown and enjoy
listening to stories. Strictly no grey applicants.
Please all bring CV & photo and rehearse one
song which demonstrates your personality
(16 bars required - bring sheet music).

ABOVE: Break a leg! The Rainbow auditions were advertised in *The Stage* newspaper in July 1972

George was sipping coffee in a Soho jazz club with his good friend Raymond (a fun-loving rodent tap dancer who, despite his best efforts, was never to hit the big time. His only claim to fame was being the second cousin, twice removed of Roland Rat,) when he spotted the auditions. 'Oooh, you can't get much brighter than fluorescent pink,' said George, eagerly circling the ad with a lipstick. His drag act in fact had become more of a drag than an act of late and the heavy make-up was starting to play havoc with his fur tone.

'Why don't you come along?' he asked Raymond. His friend sighed: 'To be honest, darling, I just don't think I'm colourful enough.' George took his friend's paw: 'Oh you are. And it's not about what you are on the outside, it's the inside that matters. Never judge a book by its cover. You will have your time. You will get your fifteen minutes, there's plenty more fish in the sea...'

Raymond looked puzzled; George usually had a platitude for every eventuality but sometimes, if he couldn't choose the correct one for the occasion, they all came out at once.

The auditions were two weeks later in a cluttered production office in West London. Hundreds of children's TV hopefuls of all colours, shapes and sizes had turned up – all clutching their sheet music and nervously eyeing up the competition. Not that Zippy thought he had any competition. He'd been to RADA after all, he thought smugly, just before he was called in for his audition.

The producers seemed bowled over by his rendition of 'Where Is Love' from *Oliver!* and as he strutted back into the waiting area, adrenaline rushing through his veins, he felt unstoppable. That is until – thwack! – something hard yet furry whacked him around the face and knocked him to the floor: 'Aaaargh!' he yelped. Looking up, bleary eyed, he saw a bright-pink hippo in a full ballet outfit staring down at him. 'Oh I am sorry,' said George. 'I was just warming up with a few stretches. I think I hit you with my leg whilst mid arabesque. Oh, I feel awful about this...'

Zippy stroked his cheek and snapped back: 'Not as awful as I feel, I can assure you. And if you've broken my zip there's going to be serious trouble.'

'I didn't do it on purpose,' replied George, hurt. 'Now you're just being horrible.'

BELOW: In the beginning...the *Rainbow* trio are snapped together for the very first time

Zippy looked at the camp pink blob with distaste. His upbeat mood had been ruined and now he was starting to panic about whether he would get the job or not. In reality he already owed a month's rent on his grotty digs in Camden. He needed a pay cheque. And quick.

'Rise above it, Zippy,' he muttered to himself. Ignoring George, he pulled himself to his full height – which is taller than you would think – and stomped out of the room.

'Maybe we'll end up working together,' called George, offering the hand of friendship. Zippy pursed his lips together: 'I very much doubt it!'

Zippy looked at the camp pink blob with distaste. His upbeat mood had been ruined and now he was starting to panic about whether he would get the job or not

People were being called into the audition room every ten minutes or so and soon it was George's turn. He sang 'Two Little Boys' by Rolf Harris and when talking to the producers did that coy doe-eyed thing that seemed to work for him when he was out trying to make special friends in the bars and clubs of Soho. He felt he'd impressed the panel as did Bungle, whose rendition of 'Nessun Dorma' went down a storm, and he left in good spirits, feeling all was well with the world. He wasn't to know then that this was a state of mind he probably wasn't going to experience again in the next three decades.

It's now unthinkable that *Rainbow* could've starred anyone apart from George, Zippy and Bungle, but a little-known fact only recently come to light is that Zippy was actually second choice for the role. It seems the producers were initially desperate to get Kermit the Frog on board. He was making a name for himself stateside on *Sesame Street* at the time, but, luckily for Zippy, there was a problem with Kermit's work visas

and his astronomical demands for all things green were way out of Thames Television's league.

At the first read-through no one had a clue if the show was going to be a hit or a miss. No one was thinking that far ahead. All they cared about was that they'd got the jobs and had all been given the chance to make a name for themselves on television. They had no idea they'd still be working together two decades later, nor did they have any idea of the bickering and backstabbing that was to fill those busy *Rainbow* years.

George arrived first and was quick to reach the decision that everybody seemed very nice indeed, whilst at the same time appreciating that maybe some of them didn't quite have the sense of style and showbiz panache that he possessed. He thought Bungle was charming – if a bit matted and sweaty in the fur department. He made a mental note to himself to treat

ABOVE: *Rainbow* rivals? Zippy, Bungle and George at the first read-through

the bear to a back-comb and a bottle of Charlie when he got his first pay packet. Later, when he met Zippy, he thought perhaps a bottle of Tramp.

Also there were the producers, the director, a group of musicians called Telltale, a perfectly pleasant presenter chap called David and a young girl-boy double act called Sunshine & Moony, who had been brought in specifically to appeal to the toddler 'yoof' market. They'd been spotted fire-eating on *Blue Peter* and were now giddy with excitement to be meeting the rest of the cast: 'My mum will never believe me when I tell her I'm in a TV show with the roadkill bear!' said Moony, gazing adoringly at Bungle as they waited for Zippy to arrive. 'It's just so cool to meet you,' Sunshine added.

Meanwhile, Bungle was in his element as he flicked through the script – it looked wonderful

Meanwhile, Bungle was in his element as he flicked through the script – it looked wonderful. Each programme was to have its own educational theme and their opening episode was to be called 'Shapes' and, best of all, it turned out he had the main part. The first couple of scenes were almost entirely focused on him. 'How fantastic and what a compliment,' thought Bungle.

The door opened with a bang – it was Zippy. He looked what could only be described as dizzy. 'I'm sorry I'm late, I got stuck in the revolving doors. I feel as though I've just seen my whole life flash before my eyes,' he blurted out.

Suddenly, his dazed face fell: 'You!' he exclaimed. George looked up from filing his nails: 'Oh dear,' he mouthed. It was that bad-tempered chappie he'd floored at the audition.

'Do you two know each other?' asked the director.

'We have met once... only very briefly,' replied Zippy, forcing a smile. He was clearly on his best behaviour. He turned to address George. 'So are you one of the extras?' George smiled back. He knew Zippy's type and he knew the best way to handle them – just be as nice as possible. It drives these uptight goons mad: 'No, darling, I'm playing your best friend. Won't that be fun?'

Lost for words, Zippy sat down and began to plough through the script. 'Shapes?' he thought. 'Interesting title. Now where am I...?' He skimmed the first page, and the second page. Nothing. He quickly flicked ahead – he still couldn't see his name. So far the whole episode seemed to focus on someone called Bungle. He looked around the table and spotted a big bear gleefully highlighting his lines with a fluorescent pen: 'It's exciting isn't it?' said Bungle, when he spotted Zippy staring at him. 'My name's Bungle, by the way.' Zippy smiled back: 'Yes – such an inventive script. Who knew half an hour talking about shapes could be so, erm, riveting?'

Next came a song about shapes. 'Presumably sung by those three hippies who look like geography teachers,' he muttered, looking across the table at the musicians

He sped through the rest of the script – more of Bungle drawing, some children on a bus looking at shapes: 'Narrated by Bungle, oh what a surprise.' Next came a song about shapes. 'Presumably sung by those three hippies who look like geography teachers,' he muttered, looking across the table at the musicians. He read through the song's lyrics: 'I know a shape that's just right for me, I'd be a square that's what I'd be? Oh please,' he lamented. 'It's not exactly Bob Dylan, is it?' Finally, he found his name: 'I don't appear until page 33?' he gasped incredulously, shaking his head. 'Come on, Zippy,' he whispered. 'You're clever. You've got to think of a way to get the bear out of the picture...'

The very first episode of *Rainbow* was filmed two days later and TV history was about to be made. The opening scene involved Bungle painstakingly drawing around the rim of a plate to create a circle. The camera zooms in on his handiwork, enter David and Bungle ushers him over: 'David, come and see what I've done. Come and look at this.'

David: Oh that's very good. How did you do that?

Bungle: Well, I got this plate and I put it on the paper like this and I drew around it with my crayon like this...

David: So, what shape is it, Bungle?

Bungle: Erm, is it plate shape?

David: (laughing) Yes – but what shape is a plate?

Bungle: Is it, (he suddenly looks uncertain) poo shape?

George let out a squawk of laughter.

'Cut!' shouted the director. 'Bungle. The line is: Is it... a circle? What's the matter with you? Just read it off the autocue like everyone else does.'

> 'But...' began a confused Bungle, pointing at the autocue machine. 'I'm sure it said poo shape.' But no-one was listening

'But...' began a confused Bungle, pointing at the autocue machine. 'I'm sure it said poo shape.' But no one was listening.

'Let's go again,' shouted the director.

'Okay – *Rainbow*, episode one, scene one, take twenty-seven. Action!' shouted the clapper boy. And they began the scene again: 'David, come and see what I've done. Come and look at this...'

What should've taken minutes ended up taking three hours to film, much to the despair of cast and crew. In answer to David's increasingly panicked question: 'But what shape is a plate?' Bungle managed to reply 'bottom', 'Valerie Singleton' and 'Gonk'.

As Bungle grew increasingly confused complaining of an autocue malfunction, what no one saw was a suspicious-looking crew member sneaking away from the autocue machine. It was Zippy in disguise! If it was a choice between a spot of autocue interference or playing second fiddle to the bear, then Zippy knew what he had to do. While Bungle stumbled off set with his head hung low, the director and the producer were deep in discussion: 'With his TV experience we thought he'd be a safe pair of paws,' said one of them. 'And they say bears are supposed to be intelligent...' said the other, shaking her head.

ABOVE: Happy families? An early publicity shot from 1972

Later that day, when the episode was finally in the bag, Zippy and George were called into the producer's office. 'We've decided to slightly reduce Bungle's role on the show, just until he gets more of a feel for the autocue,' said the producer, diplomatically. 'So we'd like to bring you both more to the forefront. How would you feel about being centre stage?'

George replied: 'That would be lovely, but I do feel the greatest empathy for poor Bungle. I feel his pain, oh I do.'

The producer cleared his throat and turned to Zippy.

'It would be an honour and a privilege,' he said professionally, his hand playing with his mouth barely concealing his excitement. 'And since we're all here, let's talk about our pay rises...'

FOLLOWING PAGES: Private and confidential: Bungle decides to keep a diary of his *Rainbow* days and laments that the first day of filming doesn't quite go according to plan

4 *Monday*
(247-119)

WEEK 10

I Got the part! I found out last week and im like the cat who got the cream. Except im a bear of course.... Anyway, I have decided to start a diary as this is going to be the beginning of something big - I can feel it in my wee-wee water which was strangely orange. Must be the fanta I had in the park. The strange thing is, I'm not even nervous, it all just feels so right. Note to self, book in for a pedicure and back wax in time for Wed's read through.

5 *Tuesday*
(248-118)

Decided against the back wax. The lady in the shop said with that amount of hair it would be like mowing a lawn. So I just had my bush trimmed instead. I am still thrilled I wonder what the other cast members will be like? I do love the camaraderie on set.

6 *Wednesday*
(249-117)

Today was the script meeting and it looks like ive got the main part. I seemed to have lots more lines than the others, luckily no-one else minded. Zippy - who plays one of the supporting characters - was particularly gracious. It really is ground-breaking children's television and it's wonderful to have the support of such a super cast.

		August				
M	T	W	T	F	S	S
				1	2	3	4	5	6
7	8	9	10	11	12	13
14	15	16	17	18	19	20
21	22	23	24	25	26	27
28	29	30	31			

		September				
M	T	W	T	F	S	S
					1	2	3
4	5	6	7	8	9	10
11	12	13	14	15	16	17
18	19	20	21	22	23	24
25	26	27	28	29	30	

1972 September

Thursday 7
(250-116)

I don't even have to learn my lines properly & as we just read them all from the autocue. Bliss! So today has mostly involved eating honey and voice exercises. Will have an early night as I want to feel tickety-boo for tomorrow.

Friday 8
(251-115)

Oh dear I don't know what went wrong. I kept messing up my lines. I thought I was reading what was on the autocue but it just came out all wrong. Must get my eyes tested. I hope I don't need specs. Zippy was very supportive, but I do feel I let the side down. It has knocked my confidence somewhat. I came home feeling rather low and poured myself a large Tizer, which took the edge off. I hate to admit it, but I ended up drinking the whole bottle and passed out on the sofa. Oh bother...

Saturday 9
(252 114)

Sunday 10
(253-113)

October							November						
M	T	W	T	F	S	S	M	T	W	T	F	S	S
						1			1	2	3	4	5
2	3	4	5	6	7	8	6	7	8	9	10	11	12
9	10	11	12	13	14	15	13	14	15	16	17	18	19
16	17	18	19	20	21	22	20	21	22	23	24	25	26
23	24	25	26	27	28	29	27	28	29	30			
30	31												

CHAPTER 2

RAINBOW FLYING HIGH

Within months, Zippy's ego was out of control – but he had good reason to feel pumped up. From the moment the first episode had been transmitted, *Rainbow* had become an instant hit with children across the land. The cast had swiftly become the most recognisable faces on British television, winning a coveted Society of Film & Television Arts Award for best children's programme in the process. With a whopping pay rise, a share of any profits on mugs and tea-towels, plus a guaranteed number of close-ups in each episode, Zippy had done very nicely indeed out of his manipulation of poor, unsuspecting Bungle.

'You never know who you can trust...' he said, pausing dramatically and nodding meaningfully at George, who was in his dressing room, delicately dabbing eau de toilette onto signed photos for his fans. 'There's nothing sweet about that marshmallow...' said Zippy, nodding pensively

But he didn't stop there. He managed to reduce the usually affable David to tears when he suggested replacing him with Big Bird and at that week's production meeting even intimated that the show's name could be worked on: 'What the flip has *Rainbow* got to do with it? It's merely an arc of coloured light in the sky caused by refraction of the sun's rays by the rain. Surely *The Zippy Show* would be more appropriate...?'

Unbeknownst to them, he also arranged for Sunshine and Moony's contracts to be terminated. It wasn't personal. In fact he'd always liked the pair, especially Sunshine. There was no denying there was something very fragrant and lithe about her, but he was worried both Sunshine and Moony's youthful rosy-cheeked charm and winning good looks might detract from the main event – ie himself. 'It's me or them,' he told the increasingly harassed producer. 'I mean, child performers fire-eating? It's just so, ugh, provincial...'

But of course, as the broken hearted pair were escorted from the building by security, it was good old Uncle Zippy who was there to comfort them: 'I am outraged this has happened to you kids. I don't know whose idea this was but I'll tell you one thing, in this biz we call show, you have to watch your backs. You never know who you can trust...' he said, pausing dramatically and nodding meaningfully at George, who was in his dressing-room, delicately dabbing eau de toilette onto signed photos for his fans.

'There's nothing sweet about that marshmallow...' said Zippy, nodding pensively.

'You think George got us sacked?' asked a deflated Moony.

But before Zippy had a chance to reply his fuzzy pink co-star came bounding over: 'Don't you just love Oscar de la Renta?'

BELOW: Heaven scent? George treats Zippy to a squirt of his favourite perfume

he beamed, thrusting a perfumed wrist under their nostrils. 'I'm getting a floral heart combined with fruity top notes of pineapple, dandelion and burdock. With a hint of, hmm, I'm not sure what that is. Bisto?'

Zippy rolled his eyes.

Spotting Sunshine and Moony's long faces, George sensed something was wrong. 'Oh you poor things,' he gasped, when Zippy filled him in. 'My heart goes out to you. But you are both so very young, so talented and very pretty so I am sure we haven't seen the last of you. Have we, Zippy?' Zippy nodded in agreement as George continued: 'Because a champion is someone who gets up, even when he can't even see what up is and every cloud has a silver lining even if it's black and I know

it seemed like everybody was kung-fu fighting, but those cats were as fast as lightning. You know what I mean, don't you, my darlings?' he added, kissing them both flamboyantly on both cheeks.

Accompanied by a security guard the dejected pair were waved off by Zippy, whilst George blew kisses, shouting: 'Believe you can and you're half way there!'

For Moony, this unexpected turn of events meant going back to school to finish his CSEs and helping out on his step-dad's milk-round. He'd promised his mum. However, Sunshine had been tipped off by one of the make-up girls about a vacancy at the BBC. Apparently the producers of *Playschool* were looking for someone to cover the maternity leave of one of the show's most popular stars; no one had even known Hamble was pregnant until the morning she'd spontaneously vomited through the round window, much to the shock of Little Ted who was there secretly trying on one of Jemima's pinafore-dresses during a tea break.

Back in *Rainbow*-land, there was a new addition to the team – Geoffrey. From the moment he arrived to take over presenting duties from David, he fitted in like a burger into an oniony bap. Everyone agreed it was as if he'd always been there.

'Geoffrey is very nice,' said Zippy generously one day. 'But I do wonder if he's colour blind? Those hideous multicoloured tank-tops bring me out in a migraine.'

George was in full agreement: 'Very true, Zippy. I will take him to my tailor and smarten him up. I can see him in a lovely velvet two-piece. I must get his inside leg measurement *tout de suite...*'

> From the moment Geoffrey arrived to take over presenting duties from David, he fitted in like a burger into an oniony bap

Much to the relief of the *Rainbow* producers, Geoffrey's arrival also heralded a period of calm – some may say even friendship – between the unlikely double act. By this time George and Zippy were being hyped in the press as the new Morecambe & Wise or the modern-day Bill & Ben. Realising that in the eyes of the public they came as a package – like Marks & Spencer or Bernie Winters & Schnorbitz – the pair attempted to put aside their many differences and work as a team. Whilst they were never going to be bezzies, it had finally dawned on them they were onto a good thing with *Rainbow* and neither of them wanted to be the one to mess it up.

Whilst making an episode titled 'Picnic Hamper' Zippy, on his best behaviour, even interrupted filming to proffer some of his lines to George.

'Cut! Hold it everyone! I would like to confer with my esteemed colleague George on this one,' he said, slightly over-egging it. 'I just don't think my character would eat cucumber sandwiches. George, would you be happy to say the line: "Cucumber sandwiches – scrummilicious!"?'

'Why thank you, Zippy. I do think it's more of a George line. Would the writers mind if we change it? After all, a change is as good as a rest?' he asked looking around at the crew, hopefully.

> 'I just don't think my character would eat cucumber sandwiches. George, would you be happy to say the line: "Cucumber sandwiches – scrummilicious!"?'

Zippy chipped in: 'I'm sure they won't mind, George. As "the talent", I'm sure they'd agree we know our characters better than anyone else. The writers may put the words into our mouths, but we are the ones who live and breathe them.'

That night over dinner at The Ivy, George told Raymond that he and Zippy had an unspoken agreement to make an effort with each other for the sake of the show.

'You are being very grown up about this, luv,' said Raymond, as he tucked into his Steak Diane. 'You're handling yourself like a perfect gentleman – just what your public would expect.'

'I think Zippy and I have developed a mutual respect,' replied George, mulling it over. 'Bickering isn't helping anyone, is it?' he added, whilst waving flirtatiously at Joan Collins who was sitting at the table opposite them with her good friend Christopher Biggins. Within minutes Joan had invited the pair to join them and before they knew it Biggins was ordering a round of oysters

for four. 'Daaaarling, you do know they're an aphrodisiac?' he pouted at George, with a twinkle in his eyes.

'Super! Is that the new ride at Blackpool Pleasure Beach?' George asked eagerly.

All things considered, at that moment the team were rubbing along pretty smoothly together. How long that would last was anyone's guess. However, Bungle's confidence continued to dip. Ever since the autocue debacle during episode one he felt he'd been sidelined and it was as if the confident, assured Bungle of old was being chipped away at a little bit each day. His once happy-go-lucky *joie de vivre* seemed to have permanently left the building.

ABOVE: Hello sailor! George entertains Joan Collins over dinner at The Ivy

ABOVE: Bungle self-medicates in a bid for a good night's kip

When Sunshine and Moony were shown the door it only increased his paranoia and Bungle became convinced he was going to be the next to get axed. He had recurring nightmares about this, but, at the same time, sleep by natural means was getting harder and harder to come by for Bungle. Only a hot Ribena and two extra-strength Kola Kubes seemed to get him off. But this sometimes meant he overslept and missed his morning cab, delaying filming and irritating the team.

He felt he was always letting them down and so every time a producer came anywhere near, he would either bury his head in his Whizzer & Chips or just gorge on Cherry Lips. That always made him feel a bit better but he knew escaping through comics and artificial sugar highs were just the top of a very slippery slope.

> Sleep by natural means was getting harder and harder to come by for Bungle. Only a hot Ribena and two extra-strength Kola Kubes seemed to get him off. But this sometimes meant he overslept and missed his morning cab

He also developed a nervous twitch. Periodically, his left arm would zoom up into the air without warning which had already resulted in him knocking over tables of expensive technical equipment and Scooby snacks, not to mention the time he bloodied Geoffrey's nose with an involuntary swing of the left paw. Sometimes, to Bungle's horror and dismay, his arm would stay up in the air and it took several hours of hands-on shoulder massage from the make-up girls to get it back to its normal position, thereby delaying filming yet again.

> Sometimes, to Bungle's horror and dismay, his arm would stay up in the air and it took several hours of hands-on shoulder massage from the make-up girls to get it back to its normal position

'I know what will cheer me up,' he thought one afternoon whilst Zippy and George filmed a two-hander about Space Travel. 'Some real air. I need to get back into the great outdoors where I belong,' he decided. And as he headed out of the studios (to Zippy screeching: 'Beam me up, Geoffrey!') Bungle started to feel a bit better about himself.

He walked down the South Bank, past the National Theatre – where he ended up signing autographs for a group of overexcited seven year olds on a day trip to see a Japanese Kabuki version of *King Lear* – and across Waterloo Bridge, into The Mall – where he was recognised again by a frazzled-looking mum of triplets who thanked him for helping her keep her children entertained in the afternoons: 'Lav, I don't know what I'd do without yer. When you're on, I just stick 'em in front of the telly and go upstairs to shave me legs. You does look a lot more colourful in real life... cos we've

BELOW: A much needed ego boost; Bungle is mobbed by fans on London's South Bank

Bungle meets his public...

only got a black & white, know what I mean, lav?'

The sun warmed the fresh March afternoon and by the time Bungle found himself in the green open spaces of St James's Park, he was feeling much more optimistic about life. So much so, that his left arm had barely twitched. 'No, I mustn't let it all get to me,' sighed Bungle, rolling around carefree on the tufty grass. 'It's only showbusiness after all. This is what really matters – nature and beauty and people being kind to each other.'

His mind drifted back to his childhood in the New Forest and for the first time in weeks he found himself dozing off without any trouble

His mind drifted back to his childhood in the New Forest and for the first time in weeks he found himself dozing off without any trouble. But when he woke up the sun had gone in, the park was emptying and it was starting to get dark. 'Oh no!' he cried, heaving himself up off

RIGHT: Back to nature; Bungle dozes off in St James's Park

the ground. 'How long have I been asleep?' Running out of the park as fast as his fat furry legs would carry him, Bungle realised he'd been in dreamland for nearly four hours. By the time he hurried back onto the set, he was soaked with sweat, his arm was involuntarily raising itself and he was experiencing his first full-blown anxiety attack.

'Where in heaven's name have you been, Bungle?' asked Geoffrey. 'We've been worried. We had to stop filming because you weren't here...'

'I'm so sorry...' gasped Bungle, out of breath. 'I went to the park, you know to clear my head. I must've fallen asleep and...'

Zippy removed his spaceman helmet: 'What's that ruddy awful smell?'

Bungle looked down at himself. 'Oh no! I must've rolled in it when I was playing in the grass.'

By this point, everyone was covering their noses with one hand

Luckily George was never without perfume and, as if from nowhere, produced an antique scent-dispenser that soon rendered the air heavy with a combination of dog turd and sickly scent

and wafting the smell of excrement away with the other. Luckily George was never without perfume and, as if from nowhere, produced an antique scent-dispenser that soon rendered the air heavy with a combination of dog turd and sickly scent. 'It's Tweed, by Lentheric,' he explained, authoritatively. 'Classic yet understated.'

Closing his dressing-room door behind him, under his fur Bungle was red with shame. 'This has to be an all time low,' he thought to himself, shovelling Jaffa Cakes down his neck so fast that if Norris McWhirter had been in the building it could've easily been a record breaking moment. What he didn't know

National Viewers & Listeners Association
The Chestnuts
3 Mews Crescent
Colchester
Essex

7th April 1973

Dear Mr Bungle,

Last Tuesday afternoon, we sat as a family and watched your programme 'Rainbow' which started at 12.10pm. And it was the dirtiest programme I have seen for a very long time.

I am shocked and disgusted to discover you regularly parade yourself naked without even a hint of shame or an apology. I found your full frontal nudity offensive, indecent and embarrassing. The last thing I want to see on my television set in the middle of the day is a naked bear flashing his private fur at me whilst I am munching on a Gypsy Cream and attempting a word-search. And all this at 12.10pm. Whatever next? Car keys in a bowl on Magpie?

I find transmission of such material for entertainment purposes to be uncivilised and completely irresponsible. I insist you desist immediately or I will be forced to take further action.

Yours Sincerely,

M. Whitehouse

Mrs Mary Whitehouse
Founder President

back then was that things were about to get much worse. On his dressing table, under the boxes of aniseed balls, was a letter from clean-up TV campaigner Mary Whitehouse.

Was this to push Bungle right over the edge for the first time?

'I'm a bear!' he shrieked, when he read the stinging attack on his on-screen nudity. 'Bears don't wear clothes! We are supposed to be naked, you horrible bint!'

Over the following weeks, it seemed only a sugar high could get an increasingly twitchy Bungle through the day. With cans of Tizer stashed around the set, his drinking – and the empty Dip Dab wrappers stacking up under the desk – started making life difficult for everyone, especially Zippy who needed medical attention when he accidentally sat on an unfortunately angled Curly Wurly.

Bungle turned to George for support.

'Change must come from Within,' George said, putting a hand on Bungle's shoulder. 'Which, I think, is near Kidderminster.'

> With cans of Tizer stashed around the set, his drinking – and the empty Dip Dab wrappers stacking up under the desk – started making life difficult for everyone

But it was no real use to Bungle because his pink co-star's mind was firmly on other matters, ie the side-benefits of his new-found fame or – to be more specific – his sudden heartthrob status. All through his life, George had never been short of an admirer or two, but now he was famous it was as if every Mary, Mungo and Midge wanted to look into his doe eyes, be special friends and stroke his uniquely coloured fur.

Whilst on a quick shopping trip to Woolworths, a busty young mum threw her knickers at him; he was chased down Carnaby Street by fashion students trying to get a snatch of his

OPPOSITE: Lady of letters – clean-up TV campaigner Mary Whitehouse is not a fan

unique colour and the Queen (and the Queen Mum) declared themselves fans. Meanwhile, the *Daily Mirror* labelled him 'the thinking woman's Cliff Richard' and it was almost impossible for him to go out in public without somebody shouting: 'Oi! Where's Zippy?' or 'Can I have a story please, Geoffrey?'

One year, on Table Mountain whilst George was mid-downward dog during a yoga holiday in Cape Town, he was even recognised by a group of Japanese tourists shouting 'Lainbow! Lainbow!' and clicking away at him with their cameras.

BELOW: Fit for a queen – George responds to Her Majesty's fan mail

'All the attention is very sweet,' said George to Geoffrey over a gooseberry milkshake one afternoon in the green room. 'But I won't let it go to my head. One must remain loveable and professional at all times,' he added, spotting Bungle in the corridor rummaging through a bin for Marathon wrappers.

However, George being George, he couldn't help but chat to anyone and

To darling Lizzie.
Best Wishes
George.
X rainbow

with compliments

Your Majesty,
I enclose a signed photograph as requested. Regarding the other matter – hotpants and a gonk should do the trick.
Your loyal servant and friend
Georgie X

ABOVE: In the pink; fur-loving fashion students chase George down Carnaby Street

everyone, which meant staying out late surrounded by strangers who fell about laughing at his every witticism and hung on his every word: 'I just think it's rude to be the first to leave the party,' he told Suzy in make-up, as she attempted to disguise the bags under his eyes with some blancmange from the staff canteen. 'Anyway, I hear it's all the rage to have an entourage. If it's good enough for Cher, it's good enough for me.'

Most nights of the week he could be found enjoying the attentions of London's fashionable bright young things, more often than not at his usual table in Annabel's, the exclusive private member's club in Berkeley Square, where he would be surrounded by his posse of hangers on – headed by the ever-faithful Raymond who was now helping out as George's PA.

A little-known fact is that Annabel's is the only night-club in the world the Queen has ever set foot in, but in those days the place was heaving with the younger Royals and it was around that time that George struck up a brief friendship with Princess Anne: 'I used to play with her hair and wrap it around me like a pashmina,' is a story he has dined out on many times in the years that followed.

BELOW: In the seventies George struck up a brief friendship with Princess Anne

LEFT: Anyone for a conga? George and good friend Jack Nicholson party at Annabel's nightclub

The thing about Annabel's was that you never knew who you were going to bump into. During that period George found himself dancing the rhumba to the Pink Panther theme tune with Peter Sellers, swapping make-up tips and political ideas with Glenda Jackson and even ended up in a late-night conga around the dancefloor sandwiched between a cackling, party-loving Jack Nicholson and a sozzled Pootle from *The Flumps*. But perhaps his most bizarre encounter was meeting Russian president Leonid Brezhnev in the club's toilets whilst the pair relieved themselves in adjoining urinals: 'I drink too much off zis fizzy Western pop. It make me gassy... and when I get gassy I get very angry,' barked the Russian leader, stamping his foot on the floor and ever so slightly splashing back on himself in the process.

It was around that time that George struck up a brief friendship with Princess Anne: 'I used to play with her hair and wrap it around me like a pashmina,' is a story he has dined out on many times in the years that followed

Deep down, George knew there would come a time when

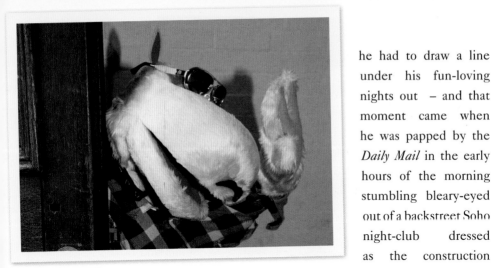

he had to draw a line under his fun-loving nights out – and that moment came when he was papped by the *Daily Mail* in the early hours of the morning stumbling bleary-eyed out of a backstreet Soho night-club dressed as the construction worker from The Village People. The next day when he turned up late for work, tired and wearing sunglasses, Zippy was not impressed.

'Am I the only one around here who is the slightest bit professional?' fumed Zippy. 'First, Bungle disappears in the middle of the afternoon to roll in doggy doings and now you're late because you spent most of last night doing "The Hustle" with a fake Red Indian and a Traffic Cop?'

'I'm so sorry, Zippy,' whimpered George, genuinely apologetic. 'I think the temptations that come with fame, fortune and small-screen success have finally got the better of me.' Zippy was relishing the chance to be holier than thou and added: 'To be honest, George, I am disappointed in you. On behalf of the rest of the cast I feel I have to

'Am I the only one around here who is the slightest bit professional?' fumed Zippy. 'First Bungle disappears in the middle of the afternoon to roll in doggy doings and now you're late because you spent most of last night doing "The Hustle" with a fake Red Indian and a Traffic Cop?'

say that you are letting the programme and everyone else down. Not to mention yourself.'

'Oh, do give it a rest, Zippy!' retorted George, hurt. As he gently removed his shades, it was clear he'd been crying. 'You really can be so horrid sometimes. And for the record, also on behalf of the rest of the cast, sometimes I think you are a big metal-mouthed meany! And so does everyone else. You are always picking on people,' he said, with a knowing look in Bungle's direction. 'So maybe it's time you took a good look at *yourself* in the mirror and woke up and smelt the coffee, girlfriend!' he added, with a flick of his hand, before tearfully dashing to his dressing-room and slamming the door behind him.

Their row had been played out with the entire cast and crew watching and as they glumly returned to their jobs in hand, they began to dread the inevitably tense days to come on the *Rainbow* set. Because there was no doubt about it – Zippy and George's entente cordiale was no longer fruity but bitter lemon.

LEFT: The truth hurts? A fall-out leads to George and Zippy telling it like it is

9 *Monday*
(99-266)

WEEK 2

The letter from that Mrs Whitehouse has left me v. shaken - hence I am now on my third bottle of Panda Pops in under an hour. How can she be so unkind? Doesn't she understand I have my own built-in fur coat? I don't NEED to wear ANYTHING!! Or does she want to truss me up in a duffel coat like poor old Paddington? Talk about animal cruelty. And I happen to know his paws haven't been the same since he was forced to wear those wellington boots - which are

10 *Tuesday*
(100-265)

actually two sizes too small. And one arm's longer than the other now from lugging that suitcase all over the place

More filming. Today's episode was titled 'Sleep'. How appropriate. I wish I could get some. It's 3.42am Maybe I'll get up and see what's in the fridge...?

11 *Wednesday*
(101-264)

After a couple of pints of Lucozade and a jumbo-sized Caramac I decided to go and see Mrs Whitehouse. But when she opened her front door and saw me she just started screaming like Linda Blair in the ~~Exorc~~ Exorcist and sprayed Mr Muscle in my eyes before slamming the door right onto my right paw.
It could've gone better...

			March			
M	T	W	T	F	S	S
				1	2	3	4
5	6	7	8	9	10	11
12	13	14	15	16	17	18
19	20	21	22	23	24	25
26	27	28	29	30	31	

			April			
M	T	W	T	F	S	S
						1
2	3	4	5	6	7	8
9	10	11	12	13	14	15
16	17	18	19	20	21	22
23	24	25	26	27	28	29
30						

WEEK 2 from bad to worse. Zippy ~~needed~~ *Thursday* **12**
(102-263)
needed to see the nurse when he sat
on a half-eaten Curly Wurly I'd had to hide
quickly during filming. He now has to perch
on a rubber ring for the rest of the week and
hates me even more than ~~that~~ he did before.
But surely, right now, no-one can hate me
more than I hate myself? Sob.

Friday **13**
(103-262)

Spent the whole night listening to Leonard Cohen.
Maybe I'll have to phone in sick today?

Saturday **14**
(104-261)

It's a chocolate
treat I was not
expecting!

Sunday **15**
(105-260)

May
M T W T F
   1 2 3 4
7 8 9 10 1
14 15 16 17 1
21 22 23 24 2
28 29 30 31

The curly wurly incident

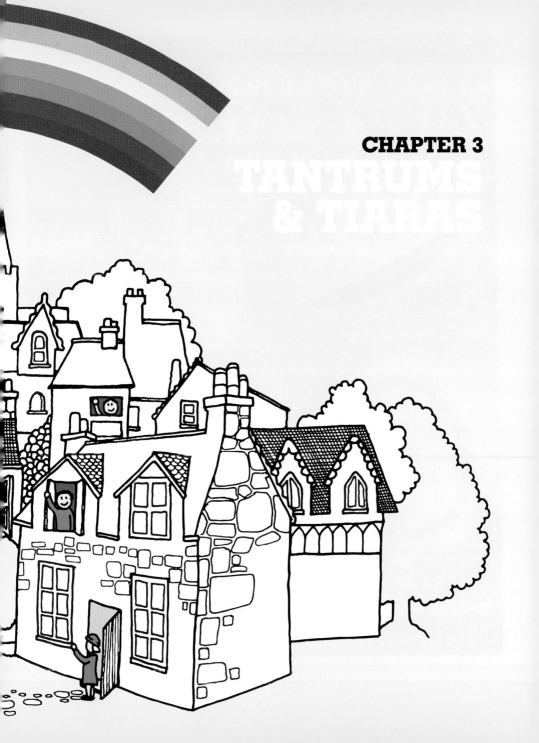

CHAPTER 3
TANTRUMS & TIARAS

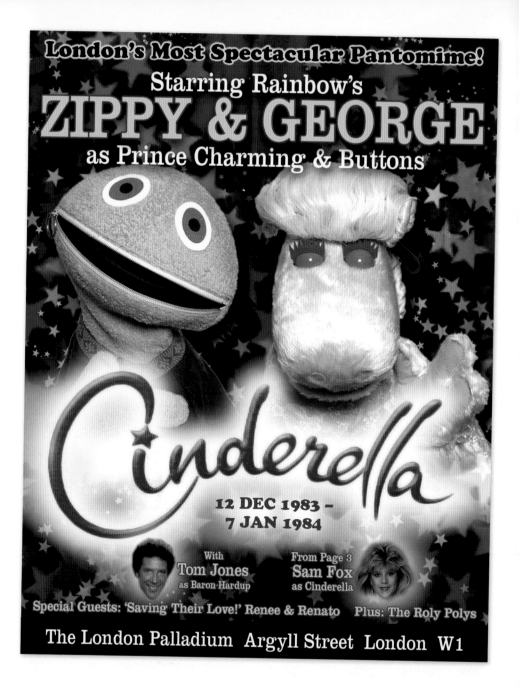

he rivalries continued as the boom days of the mid-Eighties approached – and it was around this time that the money really started rolling in for Zippy and George. The pair had the golden touch with their across-the-board family appeal and offers on the table included a top West End pantomime with Tom Jones and The Roly Polys, a charity single with Frankie Goes to Hollywood and megabucks telly ad campaigns for both Soda Stream and Shake 'n' Vac.

In fact, because he had worked his way through practically every perfume on the market, for a period during their infamous Shake 'n' Vac campaign George began to wear it as an alternative to aftershave. 'It really does put the freshness back,' he enthused, contentedly dabbing the carpet freshener behind his ears before throwing some under his armpit for good measure. 'I do love a freebie. Don't you, Zip?'

In the make-up chair next to him Zippy gasped for air: 'George! It makes me want to barf up my beef crisps!' he gagged, wafting his one and only hand in an attempt to clear the pine-fresh fog gathering around them.

Despite the fact the stars' relationship off-screen was much shakier than the one they portrayed on it, *Rainbow* was going from strength to strength and when perky singer-songwriter combo Rod, Jane and Freddy joined the team, the show's appeal broadened even further.

OPPOSITE: It's behind you! The money starts rolling in for Zippy and George
BELOW: All smiles? Rod, Jane and Freddy join the award winning show

'We are so very lucky to be headlining in a hit,' George had reminded Zippy. 'I mean, look at poor Raymond. So much talent yet the only stage he has at the moment is the counter at Wimpy. The poor darling – those uniforms are playing havoc with his fur. Not a natural fibre in sight...'

For the following year the pair continued to rub along happily enough for the sake of the show, without any major fallouts or fisticuffs. None that made the newspapers, anyway. There was a minor incident during a post-modern photo shoot for style-bible *The Face* – where they both fell out over camera angles. But it was resolved when George agreed to be shot from the left (his worst side) whilst wearing an all-in-one PVC catsuit, so long as Zippy's zip wasn't given undue prominence.

However, it was when the show's bosses asked George to play another character – his loveable Cousin Georgina – that the fur really did begin to fly. Like Dame Edna and Barry Humphries, George and Georgina were never seen in the same place together. The reason for Georgina's creation was that the producers wanted to establish another female presence on the show alongside Jane, a need Zippy disputed from the off: 'Surely George is girlie enough?' he snapped.

Meanwhile, George relished the opportunity to play someone new: 'Oh goody!' he'd squealed, when told of the plan. 'It'll be like being back on the club circuit – but without the booing. I see Georgina as a girl next door type,' he announced. 'I'm thinking Bet Lynch meets Isla St Clair, I'm thinking beehive, I'm thinking a Scottish lilt, I'm thinking a limp.'

Ultimately, there were very few differences between the two

loveably pink characters. Described by one sniffy critic as 'the small-screen's answer to Michael Caine', no one could ever call George the most versatile of actors. But what he did, he did with charisma, and the nation's favourite hippo threw himself into his new role with gusto. Cousin Georgina's sporadic guest appearances (made while George himself was supposedly 'away visiting Auntie') proved to be yet another popular addition to *Rainbow*'s increasingly colourful cast-list.

Predictably, Zippy wasn't quite so chuffed about this new development. In retaliation he demanded his own spin-off series – *The Zippy Zippy Shake*, a *Minder* meets *Kids From Fame* style drama with Zippy as a detective night-club owner, co-starring Jan Francis as Dolores, his mute dancer wife. When it was made clear to him that his idea 'didn't have legs' ('Are you taking the proverbial?' he retorted), Zippy handed in his notice and threatened to quit.

Eventually, when he'd calmed down, he did agree to appear as his own long lost cousin, Zippo, initially playing him as an eloquent Frenchman ('Peux-tu nous lire une histoire, s'il te plaît, Geoffrey? J'adore Jean-Paul Sartre!') but quickly changed the character to a brash, rapping American when it became clear he was allergic to French onions and berets.

Determined to make the most of his RADA training, Zippy decided method acting was the way forward in order to empathise fully with his new character. So, whenever Zippo was scripted into an episode, Zippy would spend the whole day in character wearing a back-to-front baseball cap and shouting very loudly in a broad American accent.

Never someone who enjoyed being left out when it came to being centre of attention – or dressing up – George decided to follow suit, spending his 'Georgina days' in a beehive wig, a

25 Noel Road
Islington
London
01 336 7949

September 24 1983

Hey Mr Producer!

It is with deepest regret that I write to hand in my notice
as required by my contract of employment, unless the
following terms are met - immediately! As you know, I have
given my all to this excellent show for over a decade. The
Rainbow gang are the closest thing I have ever had to -
excuse me, I think I'm going to cry - a true, loving family.

But today's revelations that George is to be given another
character to play - this so-called 'Cousin Georgina' -
is just too much. It's not fair! If you think I am going
to play second fiddle to that talentless, fat-arsed,
marshmallow joke of a mammal then you have another think
coming.

If you wish me to remain in my post as Britain's favourite
zipped entertainer I demand my own prime-time spin-off
series forthwith. Or else, quite frankly, I'm off to break
America instead. Let's just say that Fraggle Rock are VERY
interested and I'm sure they would bestow upon me the
RESPECT that a STAR of my STATUS deserves.

May I also take this opportunity to remind you my contract
states that if I am ever forced to resign from Rainbow I
will automatically be paid a £1.5 million bonus, plus a
yearly pension of £600,000, for life.

I look forward to hearing from you at your earliest
convenience.

Zippy
Actor/Singer/Entertainer

OPPOSITE: It's with
deepest regret...a
furious Zippy
hands in his notice
LEFT: In character;
George and
Zippy take on new
identities

Georgina & Zippo

string of pearls (borrowed from his mum, Jean) and a ra-ra skirt.

On the rare occasion Zippo and Georgina appeared together, both Zippy and George would flounce around the set as their alter-egos, both desperate to prove their acting credentials.

'Howdy there, George, erm... aaaaah mean Georgina,' drawled Zippy.

'Good day to you, kind sir,' purred George, daintily holding out his hand to be kissed. 'I'm just a pretty local girl don't you know. I'm so sorry, I can't quite place your accent? Is it Welsh?' George pouted, as Zippy's face turned to thunder. 'Aaaam fraaam Texaaas in the U, S of A,' Zippy barked back, determined to hold it together. 'Wooould you laaak to see maaah faaaaany pack?'

This all proved too much for Bungle – by now a bear on the verge of a nervous breakdown – who had to go and lock himself in the Gents, where he had a little weep and tried to sort his head

Sometimes when the arguing got too much I'd hide in the Gents and have a little weep

Bear on the verge of a nervous breakdown?

ABOVE: Don't cry out loud; Bungle spends some quality time with himself

out: 'I just can't tell what's real and what's not anymore,' he blubbered to himself.

Another infamous spat – still grimly remembered by all who were present – occurred one wet October morning as the crew prepared for filming.

Geoffrey had been thrashing Bungle again at Connect Four, so when he rushed off with a roll of Andrex for an impromptu sit down in the woods (as bears do), Geoffrey moved the counters around so it looked like Bungle was winning instead. He figured his co-star was definitely in need of a morale booster and this was just the way to do it.

'I'm winning!' Bungle exclaimed happily to Geoffrey when he returned. 'How exciting!'

'Noooooooooo!' The shriek could be heard as far away as the canteen. Zippy's dressing-room door crashed open and an eerie hush echoed around the set as he stomped towards Bungle and Geoffrey.

Furious, Zippy slammed a magazine onto the desk in front

'I just can't tell what's real and what's not anymore,' he blubbered to himself

of them: 'Would someone like to explain how *presactly* this happened?' he yelped. A confused Bungle and Geoffrey leaned in to look. 'It's this week's *Woman's Weekly*,' said Geoffrey, somewhat bemused.

Bungle skimmed the cover and his eyes widened as he spotted the cause of the problem: 'Oh f-f-fiddlesticks,' he stammered, tossing a flying saucer into his mouth. After everything he'd been through recently he couldn't face another of Zippy's meltdowns.

That month had already seen a major fallout when a paranoid Zippy had become convinced that if you played Rod, Jane and Freddy's songs backwards you could hear hidden satanic messages by the trio intoning 'killzippykillzippykillzippy' over and over again. Bungle had gone to great lengths to subdue Zippy with some out-of-date Zubes while explaining that their song about what 'Hippies like' didn't sound at all like 'Kill Zippy' when played backwards. Although, secretly, Bungle thought Zippy had a point.

Then there was the 'Princess Diana Incident' at the Variety Club Ball, held that year at the Dorchester Hotel in London. Zippy and George were both honoured to be positioned either side of Her Royal Highness for the meal, but, much to Zippy's frustration she seemed to take a shine to George, not him.

'You remind me so much of myself,' Diana had said to George, her doe eyes gazing into his as she popped a buttery asparagus spear into his eager mouth. George gulped it down and guffawed. 'Do you like rolling in the mud on Hampstead Heath until your bits are all slippery, too?'

'No, darling, no. I mean your relationship with Geoffrey is rather crowded, just like my own.'

'Oh, queen of our hearts,' he'd said, wiping away her tears with his Snoopy hanky. 'I didn't know. But like a bridge over troubled water, I will lay me down.'

When Zippy saw how well George was getting on with Diana he'd nearly vomited the pineapple back onto his gammon steak. Bribing a waiter to distract George's attention, he had whisked the Princess onto the dance floor to show off his American Smooth. When George realised Zippy had tricked him, he was distraught and had to take comfort in the maternal arms of Floella Benjamin at the next table, begging her to assure him that his pink hippo backside did not look big in black dress pants.

That sorry episode had been bad enough, but Bungle knew this one was going to be even worse. Because there, in pride of place on the cover of *Woman's Weekly*, was a picture of George luxuriating in a Matey bubble bath grinning like the hippo

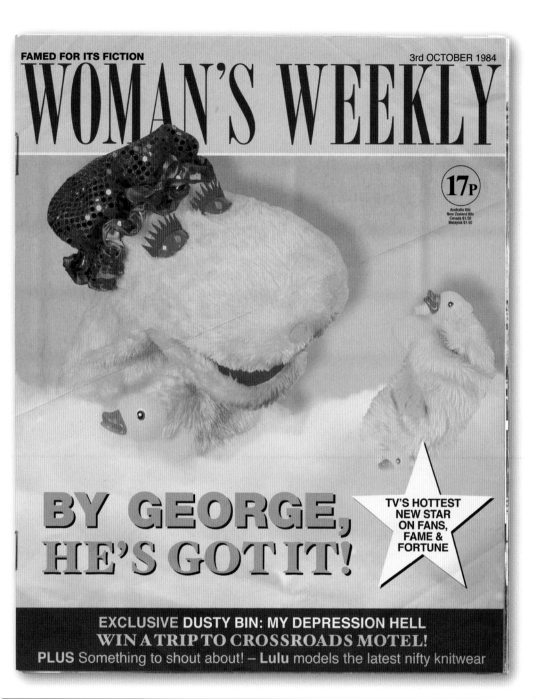

FAMED FOR ITS FICTION

3rd OCTOBER 1984

WOMAN'S WEEKLY

17P

Australia 60c
New Zealand 80c
Canada $1.50
Malaysia $1.50

BY GEORGE,
HE'S GOT IT!

TV'S HOTTEST
NEW STAR
ON FANS,
FAME &
FORTUNE

EXCLUSIVE **DUSTY BIN: MY DEPRESSION HELL**
WIN A TRIP TO CROSSROADS MOTEL!
PLUS Something to shout about! – **Lulu** models the latest nifty knitwear

who'd got the last zebra. The headline underneath read: 'By George, he's got it!'

Geoffrey continued reading: 'It says "TV's hottest new star on fans, fame and fortune." Isn't that super? George must be thrilled. But why didn't they ask you too, Zippy?'

'That a very good question, Geoffrey,' replied Zippy, apoplectic at having to endure this very public humiliation. As far as he was concerned, this was the final straw. 'Maybe somebody could tell me that?' he added, tapping his fingers impatiently on the desk.

A nervous-looking stage hand ran off to find a producer, dashing past George, who had just arrived on set. 'Morning, everyone,' he said, tottering towards them, oblivious to the landmine he was about to walk onto. 'Is everybody feeling lovely today?'

'No I am not feeling lovely, George. Actually, I'm not feeling lovely at all...' replied Zippy, jabbing his finger at the offending item.

'Ooooh, I'm on the cover of the *Woman's Weekly*!' whooped George. 'I did so enjoy having my picture taken that day. The photographer said I took to the shoot like a duck to water. I said, "I am a water-horse, after all." He thought I'd said "warty whore", and we were all laughing and laughing and the bubbles were so tingly and...'

Zippy interrupted: 'And why, pray tell, wasn't I invited?' By this point Zippy was breathing into a brown paper bag to quell an impending panic attack. Bungle quickly snatched it back – he had a few remaining ounces of Space Dust in there.

'Oh I'm sorry, Zippy,' pouted George, 'I didn't realise you'd be so upset about not having a Matey bath with me... Did you want to give me a good rub and cover me in lather?' (This comment was accompanied by assorted sniggers and snorts from the crew, some not even drug-related.)

Zippy put his hand on his hip: 'That nice but dim act might work for these telly jellyheads, George, but you don't fool me. You know perfectly well that you arranged this behind my back just to get one up on me. It's not fair!'

The crew collectively sucked in their breath.

George pursed his lips: 'Like it wasn't fair when you spoiled my delightful evening with Diana, Princess of Wales?' he said.

Geoffrey interjected: 'Now, come on you two, can't we sort this out nicely?'

'Oh shut up, Geoffrey,' snapped Zippy. 'We're not on the telly now – we aren't going to sing some infantile song and kiss and make up just because you say so.'

'I'm sorry, Zippy, but it wasn't down to me,' said George. 'They told me it's because of your look. Apparently fluorescent pink is much more glamorous for a cover star. It's the colour of love. Mustard-yellow, however, is the colour of pus. How very fitting,' he sighed, smiling to himself as he watched his co-star seethe.

As Zippy started to foam at the mouth, running the very real risk of rust, George added: 'It's not my fault I'm the more popular one...'

It's not my fault I'm the more popular one...

Take that – you fat-bottomed marshmallow!

Best of enemies?

ABOVE: George and Zippy come to blows over the *Woman's Weekly* cover

At which point Bungle decided to whisper 'Kill Zippy!' but a little too loudly, which only added to Zippy's fury. He had to be restrained by Geoffrey and two cameramen as he rolled up the *Woman's Weekly* and lunged at George with it, screaming.

'You're going to regret messing with me!' he yelled as he was escorted back to his dressing-room. 'By George, you'll get it – you fat-bottomed marshmallow!' The door slammed as his cries faded into the distance.

Hopping mad, Zippy was determined to take his revenge, which he succeeded in doing a few weeks later. The perfect opportunity presented itself on a particularly bumpy flight home from entertaining the troops in the Falklands – during which he plied a ravenous George (still giddy from all those men in uniform) with a specially pre-prepared packed-lunch. Within a matter of minutes George had guzzled down a gloopy tin of Brain's Faggots, a creamy mushroom Cup-a-Soup and several slabs of

BELOW: Something for the weekend? Bungle is papped while stocking up on essentials

past its sell-by date Battenburg. By the time the plane lurched towards RAF Brize Norton, the famously pink TV star was looking decidedly green and clutching onto his sick bag for dear life.

Meanwhile Bungle's bingeing – not to mention a well-documented fallout with Basil Brush during a fraught appearance on *Pebble Mill At One* – meant he was increasingly unreliable. Depressed and fed up with playing second fiddle to Zippy and George, the beleaguered bear – during a rare moment of clarity – had

Bear Binging!

realised he was the only one able to stop this downward spiral and booked himself into a one day assertiveness workshop in Brighton.

ABOVE: Comfort eating; Bungle can't get enough of the sugary stuff

However, the results were disappointing. For a start, during an opening exercise on the beach, where the group were required to stand in a circle and scream their names three times at the top of their voice, Bungle could only manage a garbled chomp thanks to the handful of Fruit Salads and Blackcurrant Chewits he'd just flung down his throat.

Later, during an exercise where the students were paired off, yet again Bungle failed to make any ground. When, as briefed, his slightly nervy partner Mandy – who was recovering from a recent stint as PA to Miss Piggy – told Bungle the way he walked made him look like a fat hairy penguin, instead of confidently replying, as instructed, with the phrase: 'Thanks for noticing. I've been working hard on my fat hairy penguin walk,' Bungle just burst out crying, sobbing that he'd always known he had a funny walk and it was yet another example of something he was failing to do properly. This led to Mandy – who'd been holding it together quite well until then – breaking down, teary eyed and whimpering about the months of psychological abuse she'd suffered at the hands of her former employer.

As a result Bungle was asked to leave on the basis that his presence was having a negative effect on the rest of the group. Downhearted, he found himself wandering aimlessly towards the pier and, of course, was unable to resist scoffing a jumbo-sized bag of candy-floss, which, in the right light, looked uncannily like George.

BELOW: The Secret Diary Of A Beleaguered Bear; Bungle notes it all down...

Once upon a time...

While he shovelled the sugary tooth-rot into his hairy jowls, a tatty curtained cubicle bearing the sign 'Gypsy Rose Leona: Palm Reader' caught his eye. Buoyed by the sugar high, and taking a deep breath, he plucked up the courage to step inside.

'Cross my palm with silver,' croaked an elderly female voice from within the dimly lit sanctum. Gradually Bungle's eyes became accustomed to the dark and he made out a gummy-mouthed Grotbags lookalike, clad from head to toe in velvet and sucking on a corn-on-the-cob.

'But I've only got chocolate money,' Bungle stuttered.

'Chocolate money is just fine,' replied the aging palm reader. 'I have a sweet tooth. It is my only tooth actually, but child, it is a sweet one.'

When Bungle slid the coins onto the table, she tossed her corn-on-the-cob over her shoulder and grabbed his right wrist with her calloused yet buttery hands. 'Did you know your paws are the mirror to your soul?' she asked.

'Erm, no,' mumbled Bungle.

'Your paws lift the veil to your future,' she continued, now almost trancelike as she pummelled his palm with her creaky fingers. Suddenly the old crone started yelping the opening lines to Shakin' Stevens' 'This Ole House'. Bungle nearly jumped out of his skin. 'I'm sorry if I scared you, child. I find it's only when Shaky is within me that I am able to share my gift...'

At this point Bungle had swiftly reached the conclusion that he'd made yet another terrible mistake coming here – especially when a minute later she began warbling the chorus of 'Green Door'. But when Gypsy Rose Leona spoke again, Bungle's ears pricked up. What she was saying sounded familiar.

'I am seeing lots of colours in your life. All the colours of the rainbow...' she intoned. Bungle nodded eagerly.

'These colours have brought you good fortune, but also bad luck,' she continued. 'And now I am seeing... what is this? Zips? Yes, many zips. Everywhere I look I see zips. These zips bring misfortune to your door, as does the colour... pink. Do you know anyone pink? Beware of the pink and the zips. Yes, I see difficult times ahead but eventually... you may triumph.'

A somewhat depressing reading, thought Bungle, but ultimately it did offer a glimmer of hope. 'When will I triumph?' he asked.

Bigging up Bungle

Verse.

He's the bear that cares
No matter who stares
He ~~tak~~ loves you whatever you're doing
He always has smiles
Even ~~is~~ when he has piles
He'll still love you when you're ~~ugger~~ coughing or snoring

Chorus

So we'd never grumble
~~Because~~ Cos we're bigging up Bungle (woo-ooh!)
He's our big brother and he's our friend
And we'll never mumble
When we're bigging up Bungle (woo-ooh!)
Cos we'll be there for him
Cos we'll be there for him
Right 'til the eeee-nd!

By Rod, Jane and Freddy

'That I cannot say, my child… and now your time is up. Shaky has left the building…'

Bungle was feeling despondent as he shuffled up from his seat. Abruptly, Gypsy Rose Leona spoke again: 'Wait!' she cried, leaning in to examine his face. 'You're that bear off the telly, aren't you?'

Bungle nodded, momentarily exhilarated at being recognised. 'I prefer Rod, Jane and Freddy myself,' she shrugged. 'You just get on my wick.'

The next day, back in the studio, not even a song titled 'Bigging Up Bungle', that was specially written for him by the chipper musical trio, could lift his spirits. 'He just seems so down at the moment,' sighed Jane, strumming away on her guitar. 'I wish we could do something to cheer him up.'

However, it turned out – unbeknownst to them – that Rod, Jane and Freddy had all managed to put a smile on George's face. On consecutive days, in the middle of the afternoon, they'd all been spotted by Geoffrey sneaking out of the pink one's dressing-room, patting down their crumpled clothing and smoothing their hair as they scurried away, thinking no one had seen.

'We were just playing Twister,' George insisted to a bemused Geoffrey. 'I do love playing games. Especially Twister – Freddy is surprisingly bendy. You wouldn't believe how he managed to reach round and put his hand on my red circle…'

OPPOSITE: Lovingly hand-written by Jane – the original lyrics to Bungle's morale boosting ditty

ABOVE: Fun and games? George can't wipe the smile off his face

6 Monday
(37-329)

My session with that palm-reading crook has left me feeling rather depressed. Am scared to leave the flat now because when I do, BAD THINGS happen. I like it ~~here~~ in here – just me, a crate-load of ~~Wagon~~ Wagon Wheels and my diary, hiding away where ~~no~~ no-one can hurt us. Safe. I suppose I'm like a furry Anne Frank – but without my whole family squeezed in the back bedroom with me.

7 Tuesday
(38-328)

Tried ~~the~~ Peter to cheer myself up, but didn't work. Am convinced Goblie was giving me evils. Thought My Little Pony had ~~weewee~~ weewee'd on me but then realised I'd just knocked over my Appletise and it was oozing its way down my inner thigh.

Possibly the ~~most~~ disturbing part from Crackerjack

8 Wednesday
(39-327)

I had a horrible nightmare last night! Dreamt I was being chased down the street by Stu Francis. He was shouting: 'I could crush a bear!' at the top of his voice, like a man possessed. He was also naked and kept trying to get me to hold his cabbages. Anyway, I managed to reach my flat, locked the door behind me but when I opened the ~~fridge~~ the Krankies were there, laughing and pointing at me with Pepperamis – then the little boy lifted up his school uniform and flashed his jugs at me.

	January								February					
	M	T	W	T	F	S	S	M	T	W	T	F	S	S
							1			1	2	3	4	5
	2	3	4	5	6	7	8	6	7	8	9	10	11	12
	9	10	11	12	13	14	15	13	14	15	16	17	18	19
	16	17	18	19	20	21	22	20	21	22	23	24	25	26
	23	24	25	26	27	28	29	27	28	29				
	30	31												

And that was when I woke up screaming... What does it all mean? I knew I shouldn't have eaten Dairylea before bed.

WEEK 5 *Thursday* 9
40-326

Work was almost bearable today as Zippy and George were away guest-starring on Crimewatch. So it was just me and lovely Geoffrey. During our tea-break we played Cluedo. I didn't really understand the game but think I may have brutally murdered someone with a candlestick in the billiard room.

Am now confused and worried about the police turning up.

Friday 10
41-325

A little girl asked me for an auto-graph today when I made a quick dash to Spar for supplies✱ but it turned out she thought I was Noel Edmonds. Or was it DLT? I don't think I can take much more

✱ Mr Kipling / Dr Pepper

Saturday 11
42-324

Sunday 12
43-323

		March							April				
M	T	W	T	F	S	S	M	T	W	T	F	S	S
			1	2	3	4							1
5	6	7	8	9	10	11	2	3	4	5	6	7	8
12	13	14	15	16	17	18	9	10	11	12	13	14	15
19	20	21	22	23	24	25	16	17	18	19	20	21	22
26	27	28	29	30	31		23	24	25	26	27	28	29
							30						

CHAPTER 4

MORE THAN JUST A ZIP

RELAX
JUST ZIP IT
FRANKIE GOES TO HOLLYWOOD
FEATURING ZIPPY & GEORGE

IN AID OF
SAVE THE
HAIRBALL
(UK)

ABOVE: Top of the
pops; charity-
minded Zippy and
George team up
with Frankie

By the time 1984 was drawing to a close, Zippy was getting itchy feet. Not that anyone had ever seen his feet, which over the years had led to much speculation in the media and at the school gates. When one tabloid dared print a story suggesting Zippy didn't actually have any feet and had in fact been born with stumps, the *Rainbow* star successfully sued for a six-figure sum, plus a hefty donation to the charity of his choice. In the end he gave the cash to Save The Hairball, a cause which had remained close to his heart ever since he'd recorded the charity's single, 'Relax, Just Zip It' with Frankie Goes to Hollywood.

In this autobiography, and after a lifetime of ill-informed gossip and red-top lies, Zippy wanted to set the record straight and explain his lack of on-screen footsie action. The truth is that for most of his life, the much-loved TV star has suffered from excruciatingly painful verrucas which are aggravated by harsh studio lights and the proximity of TV cameras. He has always attempted to keep any health issues he may have to himself in order not to distress any young fans. So he asks, having made this revelation, that whilst he's been happy to live most of his life under the glare of the spotlight, his health will always remain a private matter and he will never utter the world 'verruca' in public again.

As the years drifted by, the day to day grind at the 'Rainbow factory' – as he was now calling it – began to sap Zippy's vociferous spirit. Fed up with watching his fellow RADA classmates Anthony Hopkins and Albert Finney getting all the gongs and glory, he yearned for a piece of the action and an opportunity to flex his acting muscles.

Fed up with watching his fellow RADA classmates Anthony Hopkins and Albert Finney getting all the gongs and glory, he yearned for a piece of the action and an opportunity to flex his acting muscles

'To be honest, Geoffrey, all these bright colours are beginning to do my head in,' he sighed. (Geoffrey had become a regular sounding board and shoulder to cry on for the cast. Strangely, nobody wanted to rest their head on Bungle's shoulder – Zippy and George put that down to the dandruff issue.)

'Oh, I rather like them, Zip. They make me feel nice and jolly.'

'One can have too many primary colours in one's life, Geoffrey,' insisted Zippy, looking despondently around the set and shuddering slightly when his eyes landed on Geoffrey's migraine-inducing green, orange and puce striped polo-neck. 'I yearn for more muted tones, something more downbeat, more real.'

Without telling anyone at *Rainbow* and against the advice of his agent, Zippy secretly began to tout around for work. The BBC made it very clear they were keen for him to take over hosting duties on *The Generation Game*. But he felt the show's treatment of the cuddly toys on the conveyor belt was akin to battery farming, something which went against all of his sportsmanlike principles. On top of that, *The Generation Game* was too light-entertainment, too close to what he was already doing. Zippy knew he needed to reinvent himself. 'I'm more than just a wisecracking zip, Geoffrey,' he moaned.

'One can have too many primary colours in one's life, Geoffrey,' insisted Zippy, looking despondently around the set and shuddering when his eyes landed on Geoffrey's migraine-inducing green, orange and puce striped polo-neck. ' I yearn for more muted tones, something more downbeat, more real'

So, when his agent managed to bag him an audition for a recurring role in a new BBC soap opera, Zippy perked up no end. Set in a run-down yet vibrant square in London's East End, it had been reported that the corporation had high hopes for the twice-weekly soap, predicting it would become the cornerstone of their early evening schedule.

Zippy was highly enthusiastic. 'A gritty working-class drama serial? How marvellous!' His excitement grew even further when he discovered *Are You Being Served?* glamour-puss Wendy Richard had already been cast as the show's downtrodden matriarch: 'Yet another great talent reinventing themselves,' he pointed out. 'This has my name written all over it.'

While Zippy was keen on the roguish 'Dirty Den' role, the producers had very different ideas about his casting. A week later at the audition it turned out the serial's hard-nosed boss, Julia Smith, was keen to fill the cast with real-life EastEnders. For a split second, Zippy did consider creating an imaginary back story for himself involving the sound of Bow Bells and pearly kings and queens. But, in the end, he opted for a surprisingly honest and emotional account of his own difficult working-class background in Macclechester.

BELOW: Going bananas! Zippy gets fruity during his failed audition for *EastEnders*

'We were so poor we had to wash out the toilet paper after we'd used it,' he began. Within minutes a teary Julia Smith was reaching into her dungarees for a tissue. 'You have a natural gift for moving people,' she said dabbing her eyes, before triumphantly turning to the rest of the panel: 'I think we've found our Ian Beale!' she beamed.

Zippy was over the moon. Now all he had to do was prove himself on a never-to-be broadcast pilot, which was to be filmed at the BBC's Elstree studios the following week. And then the job was his.

Meanwhile, George and Bungle were bewildered by Zippy's sudden upbeat mood, especially when their metal-mouthed co-star began plying them with cherryade from his own private Soda Stream, offered Geoffrey a back-rub and insisted on giving them all a lift home in his chauffeur-driven limo. The day he brought in the home-made cookies (on the top of which he'd lovingly inscribed their names in swirly icing), George became convinced Zippy had either gone bipolar or was up to no good. After careful consideration he decided he was leaning towards the second option. As for Bungle, well, he was just grateful for the free grub.

George became convinced Zippy had either gone bipolar or was up to no good. After careful consideration he decided he was leaning towards the second option

Therefore, a week later, when Zippy appeared to be back to his usual prickly self, creating havoc on set and guarding his Soda Stream as if his life depended on it, George decided to investigate. Through his network of showbiz contacts he found out about Zippy's hush-hush *EastEnders* audition, plus his disastrous participation in the pilot which had resulted in him being swiftly replaced by a young Adam Woodyatt.

'I actually turned the job down,' insisted Zippy, when George confronted him. 'When it came to it I couldn't abandon you, dear George, or my beloved *Rainbow*,' he explained, his voice hammily shaking with emotion as his one limp hand reached for his chest.

'Oh come off it, Zippy,' scoffed George. 'You're not that good an actor. I know what happened because I know a lot of people in this biz. My good chum Andrew is pals with Guy who is special friends with Tom who knows Malcolm who shares bunk-beds in Earls Court with Benji who just happens to be the best friend of Dan who – and this is the best bit – has recently been given the position of wig mistress on your rather wonderful sounding new *EastEnders* programme...'

Zippy visibly blanched. The game was up. George had found out that whenever a scene required 'Ian' to bag up fruit and veg on his father's market stall, one-handed Zippy just couldn't manage it. During filming, so much fruit had ended up ruined that a runner had to be sent to Sainsbury's four times in order to restock the stall. Not to mention the moment when veteran actress Gretchen Franklin – who played Ethel – slid on a rotting pear and had to spend the rest of the week wearing a neckbrace.

Bungle needs a sherbet hit.

ABOVE: A grateful Bungle tucks into Zippy's sweet offerings

'It wasn't a pear actually, Mr Know-it-all,' snapped Zippy, his head held high in an attempt to retain some dignity. 'It was a kumquat.' And with that he turned on his heel and left the room, determined not to let a gloating George see he'd won that particular battle.

To make matters worse, a week later Zippy discovered Rod, Jane and Freddy were being

'It wasn't a pear actually Mr Know-it-all,' snapped Zippy, his head held high in an attempt to retain some dignity. 'It was a kumquat'

Green Eyed Monster

Verse

Who-oah! Who-oah!
He's gonna ~~getzz~~ getcha
 The Green Eyed Monster
He's gonna getcha... if he can
He's a baddie
He'll make you saddy
He'll make you angry- yes he can!

Chorus

~~so~~ ~~Alo~~ But if you want to escape him
 Just be gloaty and lovely (oooh!)
 Hold hands and be happy (oooh!)
 And tell him, not today thank you Mr Monster
 Cos I'm a very happy and I'm a very lovely man!

I ❤ Rod + Freddy :)

given their own self-titled spin-off series. He didn't react well. Having taken a vow of silence he locked himself in his dressing-room and even an uplifting solo number from Jane, titled 'Green Eyed Monster', couldn't prise him out.

It was only when he'd arranged yet another pay rise (brokered with the show's producers who'd spent three hours on their knees negotiating through a gap under the door) that he agreed to resume filming. By now, Zippy was earning more than Rod, Jane and Freddy combined and whilst that knowledge did satisfy him greatly, he still yearned for change.

However, a shouty phone-call from Bob Geldof asking him to duet with Sting and Bono as part of a charity super-group called Band Aid did cheer him up. Especially when he found out George was merely expected to mime to the chorus in the video alongside Marilyn and Jody Watley. Not that George was bothered, he was just giddy at the thought of spending a day surrounded by rock stars. Most exciting of all, his current favourite pop idol, Boy George, was also going to be there.

OPPOSITE: Jane pens a tune for Zippy
BELOW: Zippy and Bob Geldof take to the stage at Live Aid

'It would be lovely to get his autograph or at the very least some hairstyling tips,' George enthused. 'Although, he's probably never even heard of little old me...'

The recording of the epic 'Do They Know It's Christmas?' took place at the SARM Studios in Notting Hill,

London, where an ecstatic Zippy spent several hours perfecting harmonies with Bono and Sting. George whiled away most of the day either bobbing around after Bob Geldof spraying Mitchum For Men at him or positioning little wooden bowls of potpourri around the recording booth and on Phil Collins' drum kit.

Being part of Band Aid – and latterly Live Aid – was a genuinely humbling experience for George and Zippy. They both made considerable donations to the cause itself and were blown away to be the only TV stars invited to be part of this landmark event.

'It's super to be able to give something back, isn't it, Zippy?' pondered George, during the sound check. But Zippy wasn't listening. He was looking over George's shoulder. 'I do believe I've just seen Sooty and Sweep being ejected by security' he cackled smugly. 'Hasbeens! You're not on the list!' he shouted

BELOW: It's a miracle! The Two Georges are papped taking a stroll on Clapham Common

after them. 'Haha! I can't wait to tell Geoffrey about this…'

But now it was George who'd stopped paying attention. He was gazing towards the main door on the far side of the room. A glamorous late arrival had just made a very flamboyant entrance and was now making a beeline for the blue-eyed pink fuzzball. It was Boy George!

'I'm a huge fan of your work,' announced the Culture Club star, almost knocking Zippy sideways with his hair-extensions in a bid to get as close to George as possible. 'I love your look,' he added, gently tousling the fluff on George's shoulders, making his pink hairs stand on end as they quivered at the pop star's touch. 'Don't you think George is such a cool name?'

Lost for words, George mumbled in agreement but was rendered totally speechless when, suddenly, his namesake idol was asking *him* for his autograph. 'Erm, of course,' gulped George, totally thrown by this turn of events as he signed his name on the Boy's pallid forearm.

A glamorous late arrival had just made a very flamboyant entrance and was now making a beeline for the blue-eyed pink fuzzball

Not to be outdone, Zippy also struck up a friendship that day and went on to become a regular weekend guest at Sting and Trudie Styler's sprawling country estate. In fact, years later, when the couple famously set up Madonna and Guy Ritchie at a dinner party there, it was Zippy who was playing the bongo drums to Sting's lute when the A-list couple took to the dancefloor together for the very first time.

A much discussed Band Aid fact, worth mentioning here, is that on the iconic 'Well tonight thank God it's them…' line, Bono only mimes to the vocals used. That day the U2 frontman had been snacking on a bowl of potpourri he'd thought were

Monster Munch, when one of the oddly shaped 'snacks' ended up wedged in his windpipe. He was then rushed to hospital before he'd had a chance to lay down his solo and as a result Zippy's pitch-perfect vocals were used instead. Whilst Bono has never commented on this himself, years later he did go on to deny rumours circulating on internet forums that Zippy had subsequently sung lead vocals on all of U2's biggest hits, including their US No 1 'With Or Without You'.

The latter half of the eighties saw another satisfying coup for Zippy. After an appearance on *Wogan*, when he'd gushed at length about his deep admiration for 'our intoxicating leader', he was invited to Number Ten to take tea with his hero, Margaret

BELOW: A meeting of minds? Zippy and Maggie bond over tea at Downing Street

Thatcher. 'Shall I be mother?' asked the Prime Minister, bestowing upon him a scarily toothy smile as she reached for the Royal Doulton teapot. 'How do you take it?'

'Erm, milky please, your majesty,' Zippy answered, rather formally, unable to take his eyes off her massive unyielding hair.

'A good choice. I also prefer mine weak, rather like my cabinet,' she said, with a wink. Zippy chuckled, adoringly. 'That's a good one! It's the way you tell 'em, your ladyship,' he replied, winking back.

Ignoring him, she continued: 'Zippy, I suspect you can empathise with my position. After all, we are both strong, sometimes uncompromising leaders, surrounded by, well how should one put it? A supporting cast of...wets. Is it just me or does Geoffrey Howe have a look of Bungle?'

Within an hour the pair were giggling like old schoolchums. The PM even delayed a cabinet meeting in order to finish a highly competitive game of tiddlywinks on her office floor. 'Your turn,' she instructed, reaching for another wink.

'Zippy, I suspect you can empathise with my position. After all, we are both strong, sometimes uncompromising leaders, surrounded by, well how should one put it? A supporting cast of... wets. Is it just me or does Geoffrey Howe have a look of Bungle?'

Or was it a tiddle? Zippy gave her a po-faced stare and replied: 'You turn if you want to, Prime Minister, the Zippy is not for turning!' Before they knew it they were guffawing so hard Zippy had got stomach cramp and the PM had had to remove her John Lewis girdle.

'Oh, I haven't had this much fun since the Falklands,' she sighed.

10 DOWNING STREET

THE PRIME MINISTER

29 December 1989

Dear Zippy

Oh I did enjoy our game of tiddlywinks on Tuesday – I haven't laughed so much since I fired Edwina Currie! Denis says he's never seen me so giddy and girlish.

Must dash, I need to change into my new Aquascutum neckerchief, Cecil Parkinson is due shortly for blind man's buff...

Tootle-pip!

Maggie

After they'd dialled Ronald Reagan's direct line and hung up again giggling, Zippy was all for a game of Knock-Down-Ginger next door at Nigel Lawson's. But, for the Prime Minister, duty called. 'My country needs me,' she explained, solemnly.

The pair embraced warmly and as he left Number Ten, Zippy's heart swelled with pride. Who could've ever predicted that one day he'd be losing at tiddlywinks to the most powerful woman in the world? Things like that just didn't happen to people from Macclechester. It proved that whatever your background, if you got on your bike and worked hard, you could really do something incredible with your life. Striding down Whitehall, Zippy radiated contentment and – for the first time in years – was happy in his own slightly ginger, yet furry skin.

But Zippy's good humour was not to last and it was an appearance together on Saturday morning television that would eventually lead to the complete breakdown of Zippy and George's relationship, when, guesting on *Going Live*, they both fell for their one-time co-star, Sunshine, now the fragrant and glamorous host of *Good Morning Sunshine*, ITV's little-remembered precursor to *This Morning*.

When they arrived at BBC TV Centre, the pair had no idea that due to an acute ingrown toenail the show's presenter Sarah Greene was bedridden and that Sunshine would be temporarily standing in as co-host alongside Phillip Schofield.

While Zippy headed straight for make-up (where he chatted amiably to fellow guests Five Star and Linford Christie), George

> **After they'd dialled Ronald Reagan's direct line and hung up again giggling, Zippy was all for a game of Knock-Down-Ginger next door at Nigel Lawson's. But, for the Prime Minister, duty called. 'My country needs me,' she explained solemnly**

OPPOSITE: The Prime Minister thanks Zippy for an afternoon to remember

gently rapped on the dressing-room door of the show's most adored cast member, his boisterous old pal Gordon the Gopher. The pair had bonded way back, when – over a late-night bottle of Vimto – they had discovered they'd both been adopted as very young children. Over the years they'd often ruminated whether their abandonment issues as kids had led to them craving the spotlight in later life.

However, today, Gordon wasn't saying much at all. Mainly due to the fact that his entire upper body was encased in a plaster-cast, apart from roughly cut inlets for his eyes, mouth and snout. Shocked at seeing his friend in such a state, George began to gabble inanely. 'Gordon! Oh golly! How? What? Where? Can you...?' he paused, taking a deep breath and composing himself. 'Tell Georgie everything.' Clearly in pain and barely able to move his mouth, through gritted teeth Gordon attempted to reply. But all George could make out was: 'Too much Ribena... Hazell Dean... street brawl... she... pushed me... didn't see... lorry.' And then he started muttering something about sunshine which George didn't understand at all because when he looked out of the window it was positively gloomy. A forecast even Michael Fish couldn't have got wrong.

But it was backstage, minutes before they were due on set that Gordon's strange weather prognosis began to make sense, when both George and Zippy felt a tap on their shoulders.

'Hello boys, long time no see,' chirped an upbeat female

> 'Too much Ribena... Hazell Dean... street brawl... she... pushed me... didn't see... lorry.' And then he started muttering something about sunshine which George didn't understand at all because when he looked out of the window it was positively gloomy

voice. They spun around and there she was – quite literally a ray of Sunshine. If anything, the intervening years had made their former *Rainbow* colleague appear even more ambrosial than before. 'What a surprise!' they cried in unison and it was hugs and kisses all round. Immediately smitten, George was entranced by Sunshine's wide-eyed beauty and girlish charms. Likewise,

BELOW: Playing the fools; George and Zippy with Phillip Schofield on the set of *Going Live*

for Zippy, Sunshine's very presence had created feelings within him he didn't think were possible. There seemed to be little doubt about it – Zippy was in love.

For the rest of the morning, Zippy and George competed for Sunshine's attentions, mooning after her, barely bothering to acknowledge the show's actual host, Phillip Schofield. In the weeks that followed they both showered Sunshine with flowers, all kinds of gifts (including a deluxe Belgian chocolate zip and a luxuriously pink cashmere muff) as well as dinner invitations, trips to the ballet and romantic weekends in St Germain and the Italian lakes. At that point it wasn't clear which of them was going to be lucky enough to win her affections. But, as the eighties drew to a close, it was another era that was about to come to a very unexpected end for George and Zippy...

December 1989

4 Monday
(338-27)

Flying saucers: 17 Space Dust sachets: 3,
Dib Dabs: 2, quaker-pound bag Cola Cubes: 1,
Giant Toblerone bars: 2, cans of Fanta: 6,
Jumbo-size bottles of Lilt: 3 Plus — 4½ Wham bars

I've started seeing a therapist! Such a lovely chap,
recommended to me by my new friend, Brian Clough.
Mike, my therapist, says I should write a weekly food
diary listing all the bad things I eat (see above). It's
already working a treat as this week I've scoffed a ⅓
of my usual intake. Yesterday I even ate an ~~edamame~~

5 Tuesday
(339-26)

endamame bean. Yipee

A step backwards. Some horrible anti-fur protestors
screaming 'Murderer!' threw red paint over me on my
way to work. Before I knew it I found the sugary
stash I'd hidden away for emergencies (Rainbow Drops,
bottom drawer, behind George's Men's Healths) and was
shovelling it down my neck so fast my fur positively
tingled with joy. Felt bad after. Stayed up
all night listening to Joni Mitchell's 'Blue' and
trimming my fur with scissors

6 Wednesday
(340-25)

Oh dear. Think I got a bit carried away
with the scissors thing. I look like a tufty
Sinead O'Connor. Oh well. Onwards and
upwards. Be positive, Bungle!

BAD
BUNGLE !!

November						
M	T	W	T	F	S	S
			1	2	3	4	5
6	7	8	9	10	11	12
13	14	15	16	17	18	19
20	21	22	23	24	25	26
27	28	29	30			

December						
M	T	W	T	F	S	S
				1	2	3
4	5	6	7	8	9	10
11	12	13	14	15	16	17
18	19	20	21	22	23	24
25	26	27	28	29	30	31

Thursday 7
(341-24)

Woke up with a spring in my step! Quickly realised it was just a rusty nail in my paw, but I dealt with it and moved on. I didn't even pop a fruit pastel. Now that's progress!

Friday 8
(342-23)

Mike is very pleased with my new attitude. Now I realise sugar is NOT my friend. In the words of those eloquent youngsters from Grange ~~Hill~~ Hill, in future I will 'Just Say No' to sugary substance abuse. Maybe I should write to Zammo and thank him?

Saturday 9
(343-22)

Sunday 10
(344-21)

I went dancing for the first time in ages and stuck to fresh orange juice all night! Today am pictured in the News of the World partying with the lovely Sinitta. She said I reminded her of an ex, some chappie called 'Simon Cowell'? Anyway I'm feeling full of beans (mung beans actually) I really do think the 90s are going to be MY decade!

January 1990								February 1990						
M	T	W	T	F	S	S		M	T	W	T	F	S	S
1	2	3	4	5	6	7					1	2	3	4
8	9	10	11	12	13	14		5	6	7	8	9	10	11
15	16	17	18	19	20	21		12	13	14	15	16	17	18
22	23	24	25	26	27	28		19	20	21	22	23	24	25
29	30	31						26	27	28				

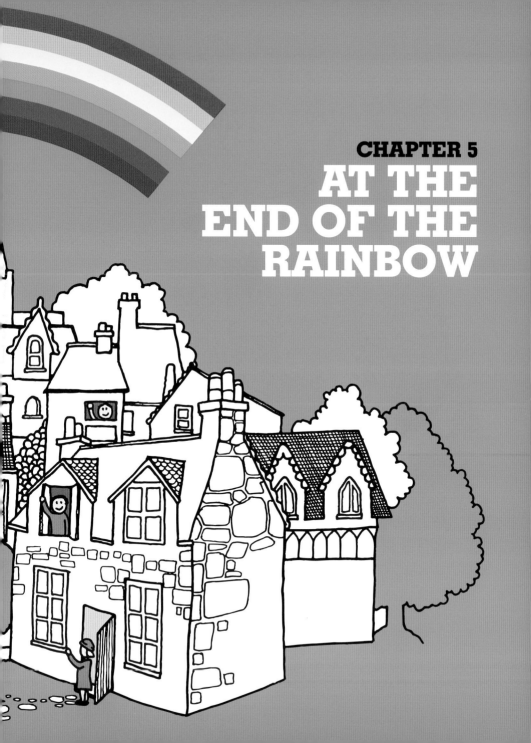

CHAPTER 5
AT THE END OF THE RAINBOW

As Bungle had predicted, the nineties started with a flourish for the *Rainbow* gang. First off, a dream was fulfilled for George when he was given the opportunity to create his very own brand of perfume. After a high profile launch in Harrods featuring the lithe young cast of *Beverly Hills 90210* in fluffy rainbow-patterned bikinis, the Tickled Pink By George range was soon rafted out to department stores across the UK. When George was asked by Jill Dando, live on *BBC Breakfast News*, how he would describe the scent, he replied: 'I have taken the very essence of myself and bottled it. I just think it's wonderful that everyone will smell of a hippo.'

Meanwhile, much to his own surprise and delight, Bungle was named 'Rear of the Year'. An honour which was the icing on the cake for the bumbling bear who'd managed to wean himself off the evil sugar thanks to the support of showbiz chum Sinitta, his therapist Mike

Bum-gle's a winner!

Rainbow bear crowned Rear of the Year 1990

Following in the footsteps of Barbara Windsor, Anneka Rice and Michael Barrymore, Rainbow favourite Bungle has been named Rear of the Year, as sponsored by Bovril. "I have never won anything before, so I am a very happy bunny, urm, I mean, bear," says Bungle. On a more serious note the cuddly former child star adds: "I do think a well maintained rear is very important. This is the nineties after all!"

and the cast of *Grange Hill*. He'd been listening to their 'Just Say No' anthem on a loop on his Walkman 24/7 for the previous six months.

Such was his improvement, that at Christmas and other special occasions Bungle had even been able to eat the occasional Thorntons (usually the Cherry Surprise) without turning into a gibbering, addicted wreck. George had also been a help to Bungle, offering quite inspiring advice from 'There's too many broken hearts in the world, too many dreams that can be broken in two' to 'A finger of fudge is just enough', which led to a rueful snort from Zippy when he overheard George offering that particular nugget.

Over the years, Zippy, George and Bungle had met some of the biggest names in the business. Indeed, famous faces such as Dame Judi Dench and Mollie Sugden had even appeared as guest-storytellers on the show. But they didn't come much bigger than the first lady of pop, Madonna, who had invited them to be her personal guests, with front row seats, at the London leg of her record-breaking Blonde Ambition tour.

Backstage at the after-party, they'd assumed the cameras were just for Madonna's own home-video. So when they started playing up to them by 'vogueing' and doing quivery-voiced Belinda Carlisle impressions, little did they expect to end up in *In Bed With Madonna*, the pop star's seminal documentary feature, looming large on cinema screens across the globe. 'If I'd known I would've shaved my armpits,' remarked George. 'The big screen can be very unforgiving.'

'And I wouldn't have attempted to get a two litre bottle of lemonade down my zip either,' retorted Zippy, a little ashamed.

On the plus side, the film brought them to a whole new audience in the USA, and it was only down to George's powder pink status that they were unable to secure green cards and make personal appearances over there.

So, it was all going swimmingly until that fateful day in March 1992. Tuesday the 24th, to be precise. What had started as a run-of-the-mill cloudy to fair spring morning was to become Zippy, George and Bungle's very own Waterloo.

As often happens in these situations, the cast were the last to know about the show's untimely fate. That day they were about to start early-morning rehearsals for an episode titled 'Noah's Ark' and Bungle was regaling the others with the health benefits of seeds and raw vegetables over Spacedust and Dip Dabs. Then

THE Sun

Tuesday, March 24, 1992   20p   TONIGHT'S TV IS ON PAGE 14

WORLD EXCLUSIVE – SIGN OUR PETITION TO SAVE ZIPPY & GEORGE

END OF THE RAINBOW!

Hit telly show is axed after 20 years!

- **The Samaritans set up helpline**
- **Schools to close for day**
- **Biggins: 'My night with George'**

NO MORE STORYTELLING: 'The cast are in bits – this is the last thing they were expecting.'

by Andy Baker, Showbiz Reporter

AFTER INSPIRING AND EDUCATING GENERA-TIONS OF YOUNGSTERS FOR OVER 20 YEARS, HUGELY POPULAR TV SHOW RAINBOW HAS BEEN CANNED WITH IMMEDIATE EFFECT.

ITV chief Melvin Brade has given the long-running feel-good family show the boot, blaming 'franchising changes at the channel'. The series – which ran for over 1000 episodes – won the Society of Film & Television Arts Award for best Children's Programme in 1975 and made household names of its stars – George, Zippy, Bungle and Geoffrey. An ITV insider revealed: 'The cast are in bits – this is the last thing they were expecting. Like the Queen, they thought they'd go on forever.' The sacked presenters have so far refused to comment, but a close friend of Zippy admits: 'That show was his life, he has locked himself in his dressing room and won't come out.' From the very beginning, each episode of Rainbow revolved around an educational theme or activity: Popular episodes have included **Full Story – Pages four, five, six, seven and thirteen**

a make-up girl, Suzy, appeared grave-faced on set. Hovering nervously, she interrupted Bungle's diatribe mumbling: 'I think you should see this, guys.' She placed a newspaper face down on the desk and scurried away with her head bowed.

Puzzled, it was George who reached for the newspaper and turned it over. This resulted in a sharp intake of breath from the trio so deafening it reminded them of the time Geoffrey had come into work wearing a lemon shellsuit.

'What the...?' spluttered Zippy. 'Is this some kind of joke?'

Staring back at them was the front page of the *Sun*. Beside an early cast photograph of them all was a huge full-page headline which shrieked: 'End Of The Rainbow! Hit telly show is axed after 20 years!'

'Surely it's a mistake?' gasped George.

'It must be,' gulped Bungle, trying to stay calm. But an old familiar panic was already rearing its head inside him. 'Just Say No,' he thought over and over. 'And anyway you should never believe what you read in the papers,' he added. As much to convince himself as anyone else.

Beside an early cast photograph of them all was a huge full-page headline which shrieked: 'End Of The Rainbow! Hit telly show is axed after 20 years!'

At that moment, the show's producers appeared glum-faced from their offices and ordered the rest of the cast and crew immediately onto set for an important announcement. Within minutes the whole *Rainbow* team were there, including a worried Geoffrey, Rod, Jane and Freddy. As the executive producer began to speak, it was so silent you could've heard a pin drop.

'I am so sorry you had to find out like this, everyone,' he declared, holding up the tabloid. 'There must be a leak in the building as we have only just finished a lengthy meeting on the

top floor ourselves.

'There's no easy way to say this. But it seems, despite being one of its most popular series, the powers that be have decided that, due to franchising changes at the channel and the cost of making our wonderful show, production on *Rainbow* will cease today with immediate effect.'

The reaction to those final words was pretty well as near to hysteria as you can get. Livid, Zippy screeched, 'No one is allowed to sack me! It's in my contract!' Rod and Jane consoled Freddy, who had numb tears rolling down his face, whereas Bungle slid to the floor, rocking backwards and forwards eliciting a series of worryingly eerie moans that, in retrospect, sounded horribly like Geri Halliwell's vocals on her debut solo offering, 'Look At Me'.

While Zippy continued to rant: 'How dare they! I'm not standing for this!' to anyone that would listen, George

Livid, Zippy screeched, 'No-one is allowed to sack me! It's in my contract!'

and Geoffrey – still flabbergasted at the turn of events – just stood there, open mouthed.

'What should we do, George? asked Geoffrey, hopeful as ever. But for once the pink furball was at a loss to find the appropriate platitude.

'Oh bottom…' was all George could sigh. The enormity of what had happened was beginning to sink in.

By now the set was in uproar. The union rep was haranguing the producers about redundancy packages. Rod, Jane and Freddy were having an emotionally charged group-hug and a choked Suzy from make-up had surgically attached herself to George who was gently running his paw through her curly perm as she snotted into his porous chest.

Meanwhile, Zippy was nowhere to be seen. However, just as Geoffrey attempted to prise a packet of Opal Fruits from Bungle's tightly clenched fist, he reappeared and banged on the *Rainbow* desk to get the group's attention.

'I have an announcement to make,' he bellowed. The room quickly fell quiet and even Bungle's moans briefly subsided. 'I have just come off the phone to ITV controller Melvin Brade,' he declared. 'I've played golf with Melvin for many years, but after the conversation we have just had we will no longer be chumming up on the 19th hole.

> **'What should we do, George?' asked Geoffrey, hopeful as ever. But for once the pink furball was at a loss to find the appropriate platitude**

I'm not too proud to admit I begged him to reconsider

Fighting talk – zippy makes a stand

'I'm not too proud to admit I begged him to reconsider, but despite this humiliation on my part, he has refused to reverse his decision.'

The crowd booed. Zippy held up his hand for quiet. He continued: 'In spite of that, and in a small victory for all of us, Mr Brade has agreed to give *Rainbow* one more episode in order to say a proper goodbye to our fans, in the manner such a respected and long-running show as ours truly deserves. And just to make sure this becomes a real TV event, he has agreed that the special episode will go out live!'

Zippy received a round of applause from the crowd, mainly for having the gumption to take such a brave stand. Someone even shouted out 'Three cheers for Zippy!' What Zippy hadn't told them was that the ITV chief had intimated he'd reconsider his decision to axe the show if Zippy agreed to take a 90 per cent pay cut, as his salary alone constituted two-thirds of *Rainbow*'s spiralling budget. Needless to say, Zippy had refused. He had to – his metal hygienist cost £1,000 a week as it was.

'**Quite what she sees in that pastel-faced, bum-fluffed happy-camper I will never know**'

Unlike the rest of the cheering cast and crew, George remained unimpressed by Zippy's attention seeking. The pair had barely been on speaking terms since, much to Zippy's dismay, Sunshine had chosen George over him.

At first it'd seemed likely Zippy would be the one to win her affections, but over a candle-lit dinner at The Ivy the potential love-pals had clashed over their politics. Whereas Zippy was a staunch Thatcherite, Sunshine was a loyal member of the Green Party and it seemed never the twain shall meet.

However, when Sunshine had inquired about George's political leanings, luckily for him, he'd also said Green. Mainly because he had heard Kermit's heartfelt pop song, 'It's Not Easy Being Green' and it resonated completely with him. 'Monster Raving Loony Party more like,' grumbled Zippy, when he'd found out about George's sudden interest in all things ecological. 'Quite what she sees in that pastel-faced, bum-fluffed happy-camper I will never know.'

The situation baffled Zippy. But what did make him feel slightly better was knowing that he had more than enough information on George's 'extracurricular activities' to put an end to his special friendship with Sunshine once and for all.

As the news of *Rainbow*'s demise spread on TV bulletins throughout the day, Zippy himself was interviewed by Trevor

BELOW: Time to say goodbye; Trevor McDonald reports on the shocking events of the day

McDonald live on *News at Ten*. Its stars all dealt with the bombshell in their own individual ways. After his initial fury had subsided, snug in a leather armchair in his study and sipping on a warmed glass of neat Robinson's Barley Water, Zippy began to see the benefits of a *Rainbow*-free world. He certainly didn't have any money worries, so maybe this was the kick up the backside he'd needed for a while. Not such a kick in the zip, after all. It was time for him to get himself back out there and return to his acting roots. For starters, there was always that long-standing offer of *Uncle Vanya* at the Pavilion Theatre, Sidcup to think about.

George handled the announcement in the only way he knew how – by heading for the bright lights of Soho with his best buddy Raymond

George handled the announcement in the only way he knew how – by heading for the bright lights of Soho with his best buddy Raymond.

'Oh Ray, I feel so down, which just isn't like me,' he said, as the pair ambled down Old Compton Street, arms linked. 'It's the viewers I feel most sorry for, they so love our little *Rainbow* programme.'

'Georgie. Luv. Listen to Uncle Raymondo. It wasn't the show they loved, it was you. And that's never going to change. See...?' he pointed to yet another fan, who was hastily approaching them.

'I can't believe it, mate!' the young city-worker garbled, grabbing George's paw and yanking it up and down as if milking a cow. 'I grew up watching *Rainbow*. I just want to thank you for all the happiness you've given me and now my own kids. You deserve a medal not an axe!'

George smiled warmly as he watched the guy hurry away and simultaneously reached into his man-bag for a refreshing

towelette to wipe away any germs he may have left on his person.

'I know what you need,' said Raymond, taking control. 'You, my dear chumly, need to let your hair down!' And before George knew it, Ray had whisked him down to Leicester Square and into the Hippodrome. The rest of the night whizzed by in the company of a group of adoring fans who were happily throwing shapes around him on the dancefloor.

As the flashing lasers blurred into one, George threw his one arm in the air and danced as if his life depended on it. When the DJ's beats cranked up a gear and Rozalla began hollering away about everyone being free to feel good, it felt to George that the queen of rave was talking a lot of sense. The stress of the day's events began to fade away and George wanted to shout out to

Rozalla that, yes, he was feeling good (as he was free to be) and right now, at that moment, he knew whatever the future held, the world was full of so much love that everything was going to be okay.

The following morning, Zippy awoke with a jolt: 'Fire! Fire! Help! Help!' he screamed, jumping out of bed to rescue his original Damien Hirst fish tank from above the fireplace. Then he realised it was the telephone ringing. Easing himself back under the eiderdown he picked up the receiver. To his surprise, the voice on the other end was Sunshine.

'I'm sorry to bother you so early Zippy, but I'm worried about George. He didn't come home last night,' she explained. 'I haven't slept a wink. I've tried calling everyone else...would you have any idea where he might be?'

The following morning, Zippy awoke with a jolt: 'Fire! Fire! Help! Help!' he screamed, jumping out of bed to rescue his original Damien Hirst fish tank from above the fireplace

'Well, Sunshine, yesterday was a difficult day for all of us...' began Zippy, hesitating for a moment. Was this the opportunity he'd been waiting for to get his own back on his love rival?

'Maybe you should try Raymond. Perhaps they went on one of their boys' nights out together?'

'I've tried Raymond but I just keep getting his answerphone,' sighed Sunshine.

Here was his chance. Zippy took a deep breath. 'Or how about Spit the Dog?' he asked, all innocence and faux-concern. There was silence at the other end of the line.

'I didn't know George knew Spit,' she said, flatly.

'Oh yes, they have been quite the best of friends for, hmmm, let me think, over a year now. I'm amazed he hasn't mentioned him to you. But then I suppose Spit's reputation does rather… er… precede him.'

Without warning, Sunshine began to sob.

'Oh I've been such a fool!' she cried, her tone switching to a combo of anger and hurt. 'That explains why I once found a Bonio stuck to his Happy Mondays T-shirt. Oh my God, he said he'd been doing charity work for the Battersea Dog's Home. And to think I was so proud of him that night… ugh!'

And with that Sunshine slammed down the phone, leaving Zippy to ponder whether he'd done the right thing after all.

For Bungle, all his recent sugar-free personal development had come undone within minutes of the axing revelations. He was last seen by Geoffrey rushing to his dressing-room, ripping up cast publicity photos and phoning his therapist. Only to be told Mike was on a week-long Bikram Yoga retreat in Mexico and was uncontactable.

'But what am I supposed to do? I need to speak to him!' Bungle yelled at the clinic's secretary. 'I've got a giant Toblerone in my hand and I'm not afraid to use it'

'But what am I supposed to do? I need to speak to him!' Bungle yelled at the clinic's secretary.

'I've got a giant Toblerone in my hand and I'm not afraid to use it!'

When Bungle hung up he realised – to his horror – that his nervous twitch had returned and once again his left arm was zooming up in front of him and refusing to come down. He stumbled out into the street resembling someone who was permanently hailing a taxi, a curious look that led to a nasty pile-up as cabs continually veered towards and away from him while he stumbled, blubbering, down the Strand.

FOLLOWING PAGES: His diary reveals Bungle's confused state of mind as the show is axed

23 *Monday*
(83-283)

WEEK 12

Am loving life again. Just say no! Yes the old cravings come back sometimes but when they do I just pinch myself on the thigh with BBQ tongs until I bruise. Just say no. Off to play badminton and then an early night, it is a school day after all.

24 *Tuesday*
(84-282)

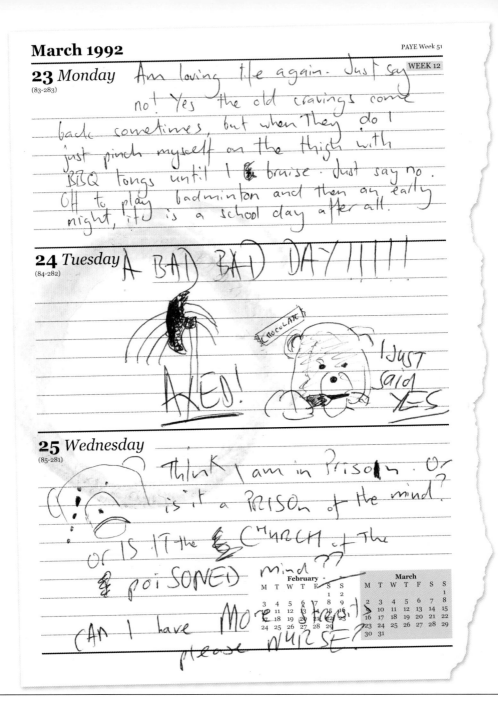

A BAD BAD DAY!!!!!!

25 *Wednesday*
(85-281)

Think I am in Prison. Or is it a PRISON of the mind. Or IS IT the CHURCH of the poiSONED mind?? CAN I have MORE please NURSE?

1992 March

Thursday 26
(86-280)

My name is Bungle. MY NAME IS Bungle.
i think my name is ~~is~~ bungle? Is My
naME Bungle? Name Bungle is my?
My Bungle Name is?
I am NOT a womble HELP!

Friday 27
(87-279)

Mmmm these lozenges are so soothing. Feel
spaced out, man Peace!
Makes me want to sleeeeep
TAKE IT EASY WITH
CADBURY'S CARAMEL

MILKY WAY

BUNGLE IN THE CHOCC-ILAT
SKY WITH CHOCC-ILAT

MARS!

MELTS IN YOUR

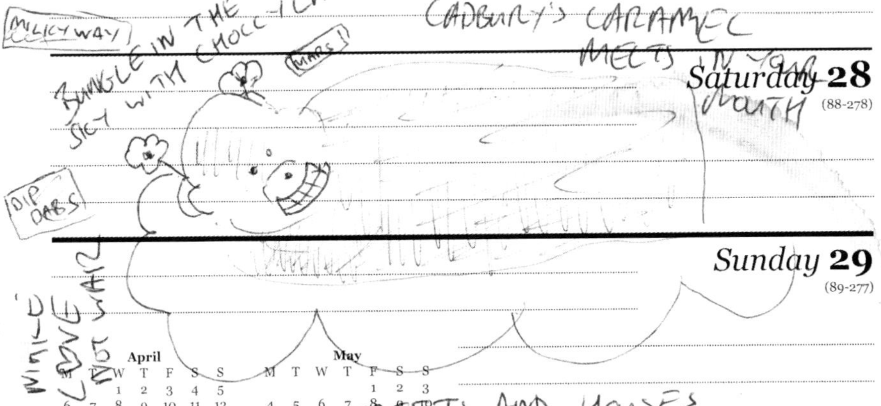

Saturday 28
(88-278)

MOUTH

DIP DABS

Sunday 29
(89-277)

WHILE LOVE NOT WAR

April							May						
M	T	W	T	F	S	S	M	T	W	T	F	S	S
		1	2	3	4	5					1	2	3
6	7	8	9	10	11	12	4	5	6	7	8	9	10
13	14	15	16	17	18	19	11	12	13	14	15	16	17
20	21	22	23	24	25	26	18	19	20	21	22	23	24
27	28	29	30				25	26	27	28	29	30	

UP ABOVE THE STREETS AND HOUSES
BUNGLE FLYING HIGH

Bungle never did make it home that night. Confused and feeling terribly alone, he completely lost the plot after downing several pints of cherry cola in the park. He was then arrested staggering naked (apart from a turquoise blue tutu) across Tower Bridge at 3am waving a chocolate-smeared copy of the *Sun* at stunned passers-by. As a result, his upcoming appearance alongside Mr Blobby on *Noel's House Party* was hastily cancelled. That proved to be the final straw for his exasperated agent, who chose that moment to ditch his client.

Luckily, Bungle was released without charge thanks to the outpouring of public sympathy surrounding *Rainbow*'s cancellation, plus a handful of glowing character witness statements from the likes of Zippy, Geoffrey and, bizarrely, Nottingham Forest manager Brian Clough.

By the time the live episode was due to take place the following

ABOVE & OPPOSITE: How low can he go? Bungle loses the plot during an all night binge and is arrested

week, Bungle had made a slight recovery due in part to several days in bed attached to a high dosage Lemsip intravenous drip. He had also been set a strictly monitored prescription of Butterkist and broccoli, aimed at balancing out his sugar levels, whilst enabling him to perform to some level at least. However, re-watching that final episode all these years later, one wonders how viewers at the time failed to notice Bungle's faraway, glazed expression. By freeze-framing and looking very closely into his eyes it can be noted that his pupils were actually the shape of Werther's Originals.

The mood on set on the day of the live grand finale was always going to be bittersweet, but everyone was determined to carry on as normal until the cameras stopped rolling forever. And you couldn't get more normal on the *Rainbow* set than Zippy and George in the midst of a major fallout. Thanks to Zippy and Sunshine's early morning telephone conversation, Sunshine had thrown George's belongings out into the street and was declining his calls. As a result, George was refusing to speak to Zippy.

'Geoffrey, please tell Zippy I don't care what he says. I know he did what he did because he was jealous,' George instructed.

With a sigh, Geoffrey was about to repeat as requested, when Zippy interrupted snappily.

'George, I am standing right next to you. How many times do I have to apologise? I am sorry but I didn't realise your friendship with the gobbing dog was such a big secret.'

> 'George, I am standing right next to you. How many times do I have to apologise? I am sorry, but I didn't realize your friendship with the gobbing dog was such a big secret'

George peevishly glowered at Zippy before tottering away into the make-up room: 'Geoffrey, will you please inform Zippy that I think the lady doth protest too much.'

The last episode was cleverly called: 'Goodbye'. It had taken three writers and four brainstorming sessions to agree on that. It was to kick off with a song ('Cheerio On The Choo-Choo') from Rod, Jane and Freddy, before going on a trip down memory lane with handpicked highlights and out-takes. The show's educational element was to be a story from Geoffrey explaining how to say goodbye in different European languages, followed by a fun game on the same theme. But with Zippy in a bad mood because of George, George refusing to even acknowledge Zippy, and Bungle far away in his own blearily medicated empty world, as they went live to the nation, no one seemed especially in the mood to be celebrating the end of an era.

'Let's play a game. What country am I from, George?' Geoffrey asked cheerily, putting on a big twirly moustache and an oversized navy blue beret.

George put his finger to his cheek and thought for a moment. 'Is it Disneyland, Geoffrey?'

Zippy rolled his eyeballs. Geoffrey chuckled: 'No George, it's France. And how do they say goodbye in France?'

As rehearsed, Zippy, George and Bungle all chirpily chorused: '*Au revoir*!' Although Bungle mumbled more than chorused, it was taking all his effort remain standing, never mind speaking in foreign tongues.

'As worn during the barbaric and senseless killing of an innocent animal? Is that really appropriate for children's television, Geoffrey?' bristled Zippy, again straying from what was written on the autocue. 'Oh and before you ask, the answer is adios!'

'What about this one, Zip?' Geoffrey threw on a pointy black and red matador's cap.

'Uzbekistan? Finland? The Principality of Liechtenstein? I really do not know, Geoffrey, why don't you tell me?' snapped Zippy, clearly not enjoying himself.

'Why, it's Spain of course. Because this is a bullfighter's cap,' Geoffrey explained educationally.

'As worn during the barbaric and senseless killing of an

innocent animal? Is that really appropriate for children's television, Geoffrey?' bristled Zippy, again straying from what was written on the autocue. 'Oh and before you ask, the answer is *adios*!'

'Right, erm, well done, thankyou, Zippy,' said Geoffrey, lost for a moment as he waited for the autocue to catch up with them. In a bid to fill time he grabbed the first thing to hand: 'So, what country does this call home?'

'Hell on earth!' piped up Zippy, enjoying the freedom of ad-libbing and wondering if he was a natural live presenter.

'That's actually Bungle's night-dress,' stage-whispered George. 'Isn't it, Bungle?'

Rooted to the spot, the dazed bear grabbed the Nestle-stained smock from Geoffrey and hid it behind his back.

Geoffrey soldiered on: 'Now, can anyone guess this one?' he asked, brandishing the rudest leek George had ever seen

Geoffrey soldiered on: 'Now, can anyone guess this one?' he asked, brandishing the rudest leek George had ever seen.

By this point, Zippy had had enough. Ignoring what had been scripted, he purposefully strode to the front of the set and, with only minutes to go, spoke directly to camera number one. The others stopped what they were doing and watched him, helplessly.

'Look, I've had enough of playing games. I want to talk directly to everyone watching at home. What we really want to do in this programme is to say farewell to our loyal viewers, young and old, in a language you all understand...' Zippy's bottom lip began to quiver, surprising himself as much as everyone else. Caught up in the moment, a sentimental George came forward to stand shoulder to shoulder with Zip and gingerly laid a hand on his co-star's trembling back. Geoffrey moved centre stage to join them and even Bungle – who'd been told by his doctors not to over exert himself – managed to shuffle ahead and stand as one with the rest of the *Rainbow* family.

'So on behalf of all of us in Rainbow-land...' said Zippy. 'We'd like to say thankyou for watching and we wish you well for the future. The only thing left for us to say now is...goodbye.'

The others joined in. 'Goodbye everyone!' Their faces wet as they waved at the camera and watched the credits roll for the very last time. But instead of the usual jaunty theme tune, this time the screen faded silently to black. Luckily, *Rainbow* was already off air by the time Bungle vomited into Geoffrey's lap.

BELOW: The end of an era; a distraught Bungle rips up his *Rainbow* photo album

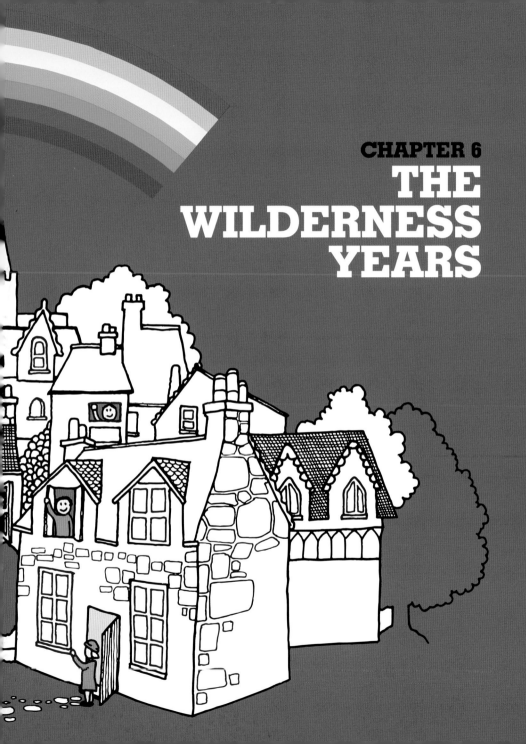

CHAPTER 6
THE WILDERNESS YEARS

While Zippy thought the Queen's description of 1992 as her Annus Horribilis sounded incredibly painful, he could also understand her sentiment. That year, in the aftermath of *Rainbow*'s axing, such was the frenzied media interest in the cast that after a month of photographers camping out on the doorstep of his Belgravia home, Zippy decided he'd had enough. Unable to set foot outside without getting hassled, he was suffering from full-blown cabin-fever and there were only so many more times he could fill his days watching Richard Madeley's foot-in-mouth antics on *This Morning* without losing the plot completely. 'I do not want to end up like that fruit-loop bear,' he muttered and pulled a battered old knapsack from the bottom of a trunk in the far corner of his basement.

His shiny mouth beeped furiously every time he was asked to pass under the metal detector

In fact, this was the very same knapsack Zippy had used all those years ago when he'd left Macclechester to find fame and fortune in the big smoke. Blowing dust from the buckles, he began to fill it: passport, traveller's cheques, insect repellent, spare zip. Then he tiptoed out of the Georgian townhouse's secret back passage (previously the servant's entrance) where his limousine and driver were waiting to speed him away. Clutching his First Class BA ticket Zippy smiled to himself – it was time to see the world.

At Heathrow he was discreetly whizzed through the Priority Celebrity Check-in, although getting through security proved to be more of a challenge, when his shiny mouth beeped furiously every time he was asked to pass under the metal detector.

'Please step aside, sir,' instructed a burly security officer. At that point Zippy was on his best behaviour having just noticed a middle-aged couple in matching jumpsuits nudging each other and nodding in his direction.

'Certainly, my dear chap,' he replied, over-graciously.

'My name is Pamela.'

'Oh I am sorry, I didn't realise, what with the 'tache and all...' said Zippy, slightly distracted. He could overhear the star-spotting couple's hushed voices: 'Which one is it, Sooty or Sweep? I can never tell them apart...'

He was about to turn around and give them a piece of his mind when Pamela's deep voice interrupted his thoughts: 'I'm afraid I am going to have to give you an internal search, sir,' she growled. For once, watching this strangely hairy woman pull a pair of latex gloves onto her big hands, Zippy was lost for words. All he could do was gulp helplessly as she purred, 'Are you going

BELOW: A travelling man; Zippy's first port of call is Sydney, Australia

to be a good boy for Auntie Pam?' and lurched towards him Boris Karloff style.

Luckily, after giving his mouth the once over (and discovering he needed a filling and two crowns in the process) Pam finally allowed a shaken Zippy through security, where he practically ran for the safety of the British Airways First Class lounge and a much needed pint of Um Bongo.

Twenty-six hours later, exhausted and clutching his vintage knapsack, Zippy arrived at his destination: the Presidential Suite of the Four Seasons Hotel, Sydney, Australia. (The five piece Louis Vuitton luggage set plus hatbox that was to follow him everywhere he went had ended up in Kuala Lumpur and would not arrive for another forty-eight hours.) The next few days were spent by the city's beaches chilling out to MC Hammer and Nigel Kennedy on his Sony Discman and generally adjusting to the laid-back Aussie pace of life. When the Sydney glitterati discovered he was in town, Zippy found himself invited to the most exclusive social gatherings and it was at a BYO BBQ fund-raising event for Brittle Bone Disease that he met the Minogue sisters, who insisted he join them on the beach for brunch the next day.

'I feel better than Bungle after a Nutella enema,' he sighed, contentedly. 'Although I do believe I may have got sand in, um, a rather intimate area,' he added, embarrassed and pointing at his zip

After a morning lolling around on Bondi with the Minogues, Zippy lay on his Garfield beach towel, sipped a Vegemite smoothie and realised he had never felt so relaxed.

'So, are you enjoying life down-under, darls?' asked Dannii, rubbing factor 50 into his bobbly back.

'It's Fantasticola!' he beamed. This was the life; no filming

G'day Geoffrey mate! Having a bonzer time down under. Am going bush with Kylie and Dannii this arvo — fair dinkum!

Good on ya!

Zippy

p.s. I have no idea what any of this means. Dannii made me write it (what a day!)

© Fair Dinkum Cards 1990

AIR·MAIL

Geoffrey
Flat 1a
23 Station Road
Croydon
UK

Sydney Opera House At Night

schedule, no paparazzi and, most importantly of all, no fuzzy-felted blancmange dollop prattling on at him on a daily basis. 'I feel better than Bungle after a Nutella enema,' he sighed, contentedly. 'Although I do believe I may have got some sand in, um, a rather intimate area,' he added, embarrassed and pointing at his zip.

A week later Zippy was on the move again and headed to Melbourne to be reunited with old friends in Moonee Ponds and Fountain Lakes. Then he bade farewell to Oz and ventured further afield. He was left speechless by the marbled grandeur of

the Taj Mahal, exhilarated by a week's potholing in Uganda and even managed to see the funny side when he was thrown to the ground by a menopausal camel at the Pyramids in Giza.

Of course, he was recognised frequently and Zippy became intrigued by the way fans in different countries each seemed to have their own very individual way of greeting an internationally revered celebrity such as himself. In Japan, much to his delight, autograph-hunters would bow as if addressing a monarch. On arrival in Honolulu they'd woven a garland of orchids and oleander into his zip, whereas in Vilnius he'd been surprised to receive a short, sharp head-butt from Boris Kalashnikov, the host of the Lithuanian version of *Supermarket Sweep*. According to the hotel's rather flustered manager – who'd explained apologetically as he helped pick Zippy up off the reception floor – the welcoming head-butt was a traditional Baltic embrace which signified good health and lifelong fertility.

Just like Judith Chalmers and Alan Whicker before him, Zippy had got the travel bug

Just like Judith Chalmers and Alan Whicker before him, Zippy had got the travel bug. But he was also aware that all good things must come to an end and after more than a year of carefree flitting around the globe, as 1993 drew to a close he knew it was time to head home.

Interestingly, having put up a united front for *Rainbow*'s emotional final episode, George and Zippy were only to be in the same room again twice in the next fifteen years. On both occasions they'd observed strained pleasantries in order not to embarrass anyone around them, but other than that, the former *Rainbow* co-stars were most definitely not speaking. When asked to make public appearances together they would both politely decline via their agents, and suggest Zig & Zag be approached instead.

OPPOSITE: Hello world! Zippy is suitably respectful at the Taj Mahal and astride a camel in Egypt

The first time their paths crossed was in 1997 at the funeral of Diana, Princess of Wales at Westminster Abbey. The second occasion they found themselves forced together came a year later when they both attended the opening night of the highly-anticipated Spiceworld tour at Wembley Arena. For George, the concert was a much-needed chance to let his hair down following a turbulent period at the hands of the tabloids. The year before they'd had a field day when George and Spit decided to go public with their special friendship and there'd been a media bunfight outside his Kensington bachelor pad. Suddenly anyone who had even vaguely brushed against George in a corridor was being offered wads of cash for their story.

Ex-girlfriend Sunshine – now a non-support-bra-wearing

BELOW: Tabloid fodder – the paparazzi can't get enough of George

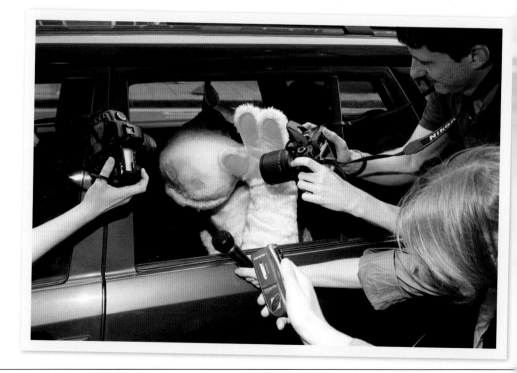

celebrity gardener on BBC makeover show *Ground Force* – was also hounded by the press yet, as ever, maintained a dignified silence. Luckily, a sympathetic Elton John was on hand and offered the furry friends much-needed sanctuary away from prying eyes on his palatial Cote D'Azur estate. But their friendship wasn't to last and the final straw for George was the drooling dog's constant need to be chaperoned.

'He just seemed incapable of leaving the house without that Bob Carolgees chap,' explained a baffled George, catching up with Raymond over soft-drinkies outside a Soho cafe one summery afternoon.

'I'm sorry Georgie, but I never liked him,' admitted the rat. 'And the saliva thing, what's that all about? I mean... hello? Issues!'

George had to agree with his friend. 'To be honest, Ray sweetie, the whole thing was starting to give me the creeps.'

'You're better off out of it, babes.' Then, realising his Bambi-eyed buddy was in need of cheering up,

Realising his Bambi-eyed buddy was in need of cheering up, Raymond launched into George's favourite Tilly from *The House of Elliott* impression and soon the chums were belly laughing so hard they nearly choked up their Horlicks Frappuccinos

Raymond launched into George's favourite Tilly from *The House of Elliott* impression and soon the chums were belly laughing so hard they nearly choked up their Horlicks Frappuccinos.

The next time George found himself making headlines was when the BBC's *Watchdog* programme broadcast an undercover expose revealing, unbeknownst to him, that his Tickled Pink perfume range was actually bottled by underage, crippled, sleep-deprived nuns in a poorly ventilated sweatshop in downtown

Manila. Overexposure to the product had left the women colour-blind and unable to register life-enhancing shades of pink ever again. Tragically they could now only see the world in turgid browns and muted earth tones. Genuinely upset, George had hand-stitched and then autographed nearly 200 pure-linen wimples and FedEx-ed them to Manila the very next day, by way of a grovelling apology.

The third media hit for George was on his own *This Is Your Life*, when a woman claiming to be his long-lost birth mother decided to put in an appearance. Until that point the show had been a blast. Having been surprised in a men-only Turkish bath in Leytonstone, George was whisked away by Michael Aspel to BBC TV Centre, where amongst the gathered throng were Raymond, Gordon the Gopher and Rod, Jane & Freddy. Escorted by Geoffrey, Bungle also managed to make it to the studio clutching a furry pouch full of Tooty Frooties and an emergency bottle of Lucozade, just in case. Plus there was a live link up with Jack Nicholson in Los Angeles, who'd happily reminisced about their wild partying days in seventies London. A rather pasty-looking Boy George sang an acoustic, slightly reggae version of the Psychedelic Furs' 'Pretty in Pink' and then it was time for the final extra-special surprise guest...

It's safe to say that from the moment his so-called mother appeared on stage George wasn't entirely convinced of her authenticity. For a start, while her hair was pinkish, her badly concealed roots revealed a much mousier natural hue. Secondly, and more to the point, she was clearly a giraffe, and as much as she tried to crane her neck she could look no more like a hippo

Having been surprised in a men-only Turkish bath in Leytonstone, George was whisked away by Michael Aspel to BBC TV Centre

than Emu could pass for a hamster. Luckily, this segment was cut before the episode was broadcast when it became clear that 'Mama' wasn't the full shilling. Her story soon fell down when it turned out she'd recently escaped from a local mental asylum and had previously claimed to be the mother of Harriet Harman, Chesney Hawkes, Lulu and the entire cast of *Baywatch*.

Unfortunately, Zippy had been unable to attend George's *This Is Your Life* due to a serious bout of man-flu (ie there was no way he was going to go on prime-time TV and gush over that 'Hippo-Hasbeen'). He chose to spend the evening enjoying a hot soak with the first *Harry Potter* and a Radox infusion instead.

By this stage, Zippy had decided to concentrate on his business interests, rather than his fading entertainment career. Having received positive reviews for his one-man show *Othello & Me* at the Edinburgh Festival, his most recent theatrical outing – a regional tour of *No Zips Please We're British!* – was less successful and ended up being cancelled due to poor ticket sales. Instead, a canny Zippy (now a fervent New Labour supporter) focused

First Avenue Entertainment presents

ZIPS WE'RE

A brand new haberdashery comedy by Roy Gooney

Starring **ZIPPY** as Lord Chumley

SU POLLARD

JEREMY SPAKE

CANCELLED

...st
...Theatre, Worthing
...Park Theatre, Eastbourne
...eatre Royal, Brighton

his energies on his ever expanding property empire. As the years passed, he snapped up many of London's landmark buildings at bargain prices, including the Gherkin, the Savoy Hotel and the disabled toilets at Marble Arch tube station. He'd also acquired the whole of his home town of Macclechester and was in the process of having it flattened and turned into a world-class golf course and correctional facility.

The wilderness years proved to be less kind to poor old Bungle. In an attempt to address his self-esteem issues he joined a pacifist vegan commune in Cornwall – but they didn't like him much either. This was mainly due to his refusal to drink their home-made lentil chai, opting instead to down several extra-large bottles of Tab Clear and doing a raucous one bear conga through the middle of an early morning group meditation session.

In an attempt to address his self-esteem levels he joined a pacifist vegan commune in Cornwall – but they didn't like him much either

Because of his continued refusal to seek much-needed professional help, Bungle's nice-guy image began to unravel. He was all over the papers thanks to a bizarre appearance with Chris Evans on *TFI Friday* where, having downed fifteen shots of Sunny Delight beforehand in the green room, he slurred incoherently throughout the interview and made a decidedly off-colour joke about Robson & Jerome, which later resulted in an investigation by the Broadcasting Standards Commission.

His behaviour had deteriorated further by the time he began to spend time with a party-loving Robbie Williams (who had just quit Take That). For a while Bungle seemed hell-bent on alienating everyone around him.

Despite offers of help from the likes of George Best and Keith Chegwin, an addled Bungle continued to battle with his

OPPOSITE: Put a zip in it; Zippy's tour is cancelled due to poor ticket sales

ABOVE: Mad
for it! Bad boy
Bungle and Robbie
Williams get the
party started

demons. The beleaguered bear reached an all time low when he went on a forty-eight-hour Creme Egg binge at the Glastonbury festival, stormed the Pyramid stage during Oasis's set and, mistaking him for a giant Sherbet Dip, passionately licked Liam Gallagher's face. Despite a mass booing by the crowd, it took several security men to remove hyper-manic Bungle – who by this point was playing air-guitar and shouting: 'Mad for it!' at anyone who would listen. He was later temporarily sectioned for his own safety.

When Geoffrey visited him in hospital he was dismayed to find a glazed, tear-stained Bungle huddled in a corner, sitting in a pool of his own stagnant Lilt, staring into space singing the theme tune to *Surprise Surprise*. But perhaps the most upsetting moment of all for Geoffrey was when Bungle failed to recognise him and kept asking if it was time for his bed-bath – thinking his friend was merely another hospital orderly.

However, over the year that followed, slowly but surely, Bungle began to address his issues aided by daily one-on-one sessions with a counsellor, regular Steffi Graf Shock Therapy (similar to electric shock treatment but involving tennis racquets instead) and an intense course of physical exercise which included rounders, curling and underwater origami.

After six months at the one-stop convenience store, Bungle was ready for another challenge and was chuffed to land the prestigious role of Assistant Processed Meats Supervisor at a nearby branch of Aldi

Sadly, by the time he was released from hospital Bungle had become persona non grata in the world of showbusiness. Penniless and homeless, having failed to keep up his mortgage payments and without even a one pound coin to his name, Bungle knew if he was going to rebuild his life, then he'd have to look at alternative means of employment.

By the late nineties he was living on benefits and renting a windowless Hackney bedsit accessed only by an alleyway which seemed to be permanently strewn with used lollipop sticks and empty Irn-Bru cans. So, while it wasn't quite on a par with finding out he'd got the *Rainbow* gig, when Bungle did finally manage to bag some shifts stacking shelves at his local Costcutter he felt it was at least a step in the right direction.

After six months at the one-stop convenience store, Bungle was ready for another challenge and was chuffed to land the prestigious role of Assistant Processed Meats Supervisor at a nearby branch of Aldi. When the kindly manager – a sympathetic

former *Rainbow* fan – discreetly took him to one side and gently explained that they couldn't have a naked bear wandering around the store, Bungle even swallowed his pride and agreed to wear the ill-fitting polyester uniform. Within weeks of joining the Aldi team, it looked like a glimmer of Bungle's long-lost self-confidence was beginning to rear its head again. But of course, along with the highs came the lows, when he'd feel the weight of his failure crashing down around him and it was then that the proximity of cheap Dutch chocolate became almost impossible to bear.

Once he was aimlessly pricing up a crate of tinned Bavarian salamis when he found himself being stared at by a couple of teenage boys wearing baseball caps and jeans so baggy he could see their Bart Simpson underpants.

ABOVE & OPPOSITE: Down to earth with a bump; Bungle makes ends meet as a shelf stacker

'Didn't you used to be Bungle, innit?' one of them asked. Bungle shook his head and carried on with what he was doing.

'Nah, it is you!' the teen continued, excitedly prodding his mate. 'I remember you from when I was a kid. Off the telly yeah. With that Zippy gangsta and the headcase hippo. What you doing workin' here, bro?'

Bungle looked at him blankly. 'I'm sorry, I think you must have me confused with someone else...' he replied, grabbing his pricing-gun and hot-footing it to the stockroom for a much needed blub.

'Nah it is you!' the teen continued, excitedly prodding his mate. 'I remember you from when I was a kid. Off the telly yeah. With that Zippy gangsta and the headcase hippo. What you doing workin' here, bro?'

Another time, a mortified Bungle spotted Rod, Jane and Freddy entering the store and panicked. He didn't want them to see how far he'd fallen. So he hastily ditched his uniform, grabbed a basket and quickly filled it with whatever was closest to hand (which turned out to be denture cream and Aldi own brand pantyliners) before feigning surprise at bumping into the trio. After lots of hugs and kisses, laughter at the coincidence and tears of joy from Freddy at being reunited with a much-loved old friend, they all enthusiastically agreed to meet up at Jane's favourite Sushi restaurant in Hampstead the following weekend. But Bungle knew he wouldn't go – he wasn't part of their showbiz world anymore. As far as Bungle was concerned, Rod, Jane and Freddy were his past. For the foreseeable future his life was going to consist of stacking cans of low-price German bratwurst onto the shelves of a budget supermarket, whilst asking himself where exactly it had all gone wrong...

OPPOSITE:
Sectioning secrets;
An exclusive peek
at Bungle's mental
health records

Princess Anne Psychiatric Hospital
Southwark
London

PATIENT PSYCHIATRIC REPORT

HOSPITAL NUMBER OF PATIENT: P542464

NAME OF PATIENT: Bungle Bear

DATE OF ARRIVAL: Sectioned under the the Mental Health Act (1983) on 21/06/96

DATE OF THIS REPORT: 25/10/96

OBSERVATIONS:
Incident on Mon at 6.47am when the patient appeared confused and proceeded to smear walls with remnants of a Mint Aero he had smuggled into the compound.
On Tuesday seemed convinced he was the Honey Monster. (A fictional character used to advertise breakfast cereal). By Wed was claiming to be a Nolan – the patient wasn't sure if he was Linda or Coleen. But definitely not Bernie. Psychosis?
Fri: Broke down again during basket weaving. Kept saying he 'wanted Geoffrey'. Father & Son/Oedipus complex?

SUMMARY OF CONDITION:
Total fruitcake Some improvement. Needs constant supervision. Keep away from the biscuit barrel.

Dr Sharm Al-Sheikh MB, BS, FRCPsych

CHAPTER 7
BACK FUR GOOD

The noughties proved to be a somewhat happier time for Zippy, George and Bungle. Luckily for them, the nation was on a nostalgia trip and it seemed everybody wanted a little piece of their retro *Rainbow* fur.

Constantly in demand on chat shows and at celebrity parties, George had become something of a Biggins-figure, a national treasure much loved by the public and his peers alike. His acclaimed portrayal of Widow Twankey in a sell-out *Aladdin* at the Old Vic had led to an approach from Disney asking him to provide the voice of Aunt Sally in their big screen animated adaptation of *Worzel Gummidge* – alongside John Travolta in the title role – which is due for release in 2012.

He even spent a summer as an honorary Loose Woman, on the ITV1 daytime talk show, filling in for his pal, Jane McDonald, who'd been laid low thanks to a mysterious sequin-related illness. Now a full-time property tycoon and philanthropist, Zippy had

BELOW: One of the girls; George becomes an honorary Loose Woman

ABOVE: Friend of the stars – George and the Beckhams admire their own reflections

gone straight in at number 666 on *The Sunday Times* Rich List whilst Bungle had re-entered the world of showbusiness when he'd realised he could make a living appearing in a new genre of programming which was sweeping the nation: Reality TV.

Soon everybody wanted to be in on the *Rainbow* act. Barack and Michelle Obama revealed in *Vanity Fair* that their daughters Malia and Sasha were obsessed with their DVD boxset, David Beckham let slip that his nickname at school had been 'Bungle' and Lily Allen admitted on her Facebook page that she'd had a teenage crush on both George and Geoffrey. Stephen Fry's Twittering about their every move resulted in even more column inches and high-trousered guru Simon Cowell invited them to be guest

Bungle had re-entered the world of showbusiness when he'd realised he could make a living appearing in a new genre of programming which was sweeping the nation: Reality TV

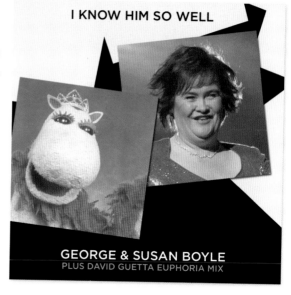

I KNOW HIM SO WELL

GEORGE & SUSAN BOYLE
PLUS DAVID GUETTA EUPHORIA MIX

judges on that year's *X Factor*. But what of the six-figure offers to appear on *I'm A Celebrity…Get Me Out Of Here?*

'Two weeks living in a jungle surrounded by creepy crawlies doesn't sounds like much fun to me,' George wrote in an email to Geoffrey. 'It's a bit demeaning, don't you think, luv? My people have spent the past 50 years fighting for the right for running water and electricity. I just feel this would be a step backwards for hippos everywhere. And anyway, where would I plug in my curling tongs?' he asked, before adding a smiley face and pressing send.

But the pair did agree to appear together on *The Weakest Link*, *Friday Night with Jonathan Ross* and (much to Zippy's delight) a big-budget BBC One drama, *Ashes To Ashes*. Despite the fact that the rivals only communicated via their agents, these PA's went without a hitch and no one seemed to notice the double act would never actually acknowledge each other.

The pair were also making headlines individually. George and Susan Boyle's cover version of 'I Know Him So Well' had reached number one in the download charts and the new bezzie mates were regularly papped out on the town with showbiz pals Paul O'Grady and Cilla Black. Meanwhile, Zippy had been spotted sneaking out of Number Ten in the early hours of the morning, leading to speculation in the financial press that he was about to be offered a role in government by the Prime Minister. Controversially, three weeks later he was made a high-profile

OPPOSITE: The reunited duo steal the show on *The Weakest Link* and Zippy loves the sound of his own voice on *Friday Night With Jonathan Ross*

Zippy denies appointment is stunt

By Mark Horner
City Editor

PROPERTY magnate and former *Rainbow* star Zippy has denied that his appointment today as a Special Business Advisor to the Treasury is a publicity stunt, insisting he was not the "type of person to be used". Zippy said he had accepted the new role as the government's top business expert for "the need of the country". He also told BBC1's *The Andrew Marr Show* that the Prime Minister was considering several new recession-beating policies suggested by him during private discussions at Number 10 earlier this week: "I told Gordon straight – bring back novelty piggy banks and let's tax the Teletubbies! He knew I was talking sense..." The television star and multimillionaire businessman is said to be considering legal action after being described in one newspaper as an "Alan Sugar wannabe". Zippy is reported to have already contacted celebrity lawyer Fiona Shackleton to see if he has a case.

ZIPPED OFF: Former actor demands... "tax the Teletubbies!"

Special Business Advisor to the Treasury.

'Zipping up our peggy purses is the only way for the rich to beat the credit crunch,' he declared at a Downing Street press conference. 'Bring back novelty piggy banks and let's tax the Teletubbies!' Indeed, tough times called for a tough stance and Zippy was convinced he was the man for the job.

However the passing of time had not been quite so satisfying for Bungle, who was making a living lurching from one low-rating reality show to another. It mostly paid the bills, but sometimes he did think being back stacking shelves at Aldi would be infinitely preferable to the humiliation he was forced to endure on these programmes.

On the plus side, he'd managed to stay clean and had released his own self-help DVD 'Bear Hug Yourself: Finding Your Inner Cub' which was followed by an appearance on Peter Kay's Comic Relief 'Amarillo' video. He nearly found himself having a relapse when he instinctively reached for a bag of Revels in Superdrug one afternoon after a particularly stressful week on Channel Five's *Celebrity Abattoir*, which was eventually won by Jackie Stallone, who'd proved herself to be a natural

OPPOSITE: Back in business: Bungle promotes his inspirational self-help DVD

◀ ▶ ⌂ + tw http://twooter.com/george   ⟳   🔍▾ Goggle

George

Oooh the limo is here – will twoot from the after–party. Wish me luck everyone!
4:50 PM Aug 23rd from web

Speech rehearsed and word-perfect. Zippy better behave himself
3:16 PM Aug 23rd from web

Ugh – got fluff everywhere thanks to overzealous exfoliation.
2:57 PM Aug 23rd from Twootdock

Moisturising and plucking.
2:34 PM Aug 23rd from Twootdock

@schofe Still no call from This Morning press office – don't you want me on the couch tomorrow, Pip?
10:05 AM Aug 23rd from web

@stephenfry will you be at the NAFTAs? See you there luv
8:43 AM Aug 23rd from web

It's the big day. Hurrah for me!
6:32 AM Aug 23rd from web

Will my pink shoes clash?
10:19 PM Aug 22nd from web

Can't decide on awards outfit. Tiara or dickie bow? Would both be too much? Help!
10:15 PM Aug 22nd from Twootdock

@vee_jay I love you too. Thanking you for your good luck message – it's sooo nice to hear from our lovely fans. See you at the stage door!
7:52 PM Aug 22nd from web

Only 24 hours until we get our Lifetime Achievement award – OMG! Shopping with Brad for waterproof mascara. It's going to be an emotional one darlings
4:00 PM Aug 22nd from web

Pink furry animals
Great Georges

Name Georgie–Porgie
Location London
Bio National Treasure

129   10,345,093
following   followers

Twoots: 6,481

Search tip
Use a minus sign immediately before any words you want
excluded in results. Example: George -Zippy **will find twoots containing "George" but not "Zippy".**

Join the conversation
Sign up now **to contribute to what's going on in your world and to filter your view of Twooter down to the people and topics that interest you most.**

when it came to wielding a freshly-oiled meat cleaver.

Just to be sure he wasn't about to give in to temptation again, Bungle booked himself in for a long weekend at The Priory and also started regular sessions with his old therapist Mike. At the same time he attended his local branch of H.A. (Haribo Anonymous) and found that Yogalates helped him relax whenever he felt the urge to splurge on chocolates. His most recent appearance on TV was being chased across a South African game reserve by Jodie Marsh on Sky One's *Celebrity Safari Hunt*.

Surprised but delighted to hear about the Lifetime Achievement Award, the only downside for the trio was it meant having to spend time with each other again. Something that was to prove particularly challenging for Bungle, who hadn't had any contact with his former co-stars since they'd filmed *Rainbow*'s final episode seventeen years before. Although that's not strictly true, there was the begging letter he'd written to Zippy in the late nineties asking for a small loan until his next housing benefit came through. Bungle had been rather peeved by Zippy's response – a standard letter thanking him for his interest plus a signed photo of the tin-toothed twerp with his arm around none other than Nelson Mandela.

Surprised but delighted to hear about the Lifetime Achievement Award, the only downside for the trio was it meant having to spend time with each other again

Zippy had met the South African leader after The Zippy Foundation had been directly approached by the great man himself and asked to fund a new primary school in one of the most deprived areas of Johannesburg.

'My country can only thank you for all you have done for us,' said Nelson.

OPPOSITE: A message to you; an excited George keeps his fanbase in the loop

'It's my pleasure sir,' replied Zippy. 'Or should I call you Madiba?'

'Oh call me Nelly, everyone else does. Now, my friend Sting tells me you are a dab hand on the African drums,' he smiled, gesturing towards two sets of bongos positioned on either side of his desk. 'Do you by any chance know Lady Gaga's "Poker Face"?'

'You hum it and I'll bong it, Nelly!' smiled Zippy, eagerly. Yet again, he was experiencing a pinch-me I'm dreaming moment and enjoying every second.

The award ceremony was held on a sweltering August evening and the trio fanned themselves with their invitations as they approached The Royal Festival Hall on London's South Bank, where their top secret appearance was due to take place.

National Academy of Film & Television Arts

Cordially Invites

Zippy, George and Bungle

To Attend The

63rd Annual

Nafta Awards

Sunday 23 August 2009 – 6.00pm
The Royal Festival Hall, Belvedere Road, London
Strictly Black Tie/Cocktail Fur   RSVP

VIP After-Show Party to include live performances from Kanye West (TBC) and The Nolans

From: Zippy <zippy@thezippyfoundation.com>
Subject: **Re: Awards**
Date: July 27, 2009 16:53
To: Felicity Babbington-Smythe <felicity.babbingtonsmythe@nafta.co.uk>
Cc: George <george@tickledpink.com, Bungle <bbear1792@b3internet.co.uk>

WHAT THE MUTHAFLIP?!! I DON'T THINK SO!!! I can tell you now lady, there is no way any of us will be sharing anything other than this poxy award. I don't care about your 'restrictions' – Leona Lewis can attach her hairpiece in a skip for all I care. I'm not coming unless I get the STAR dressing room. Geddit? FYI I'm guessing the hippo will also want his own space and I'm sure Bungle can make do in the Gents. Now get your people to speak to my people. I really haven't got time for this!

Zippy
CEO, The Zippy Foundation & ZPY Property Inc
30 St Mary Axe, London

on 27 July 2009, at 16:50, Felicity Babbington-Smythe wrote:

Zippy, many thanks for getting back to me so promptly. Regarding your dressing room, due to space restrictions we've put you in with George and Bungle. Hope that's ok? We thought it'd be fun for you all and you'd be able to comb each others back-hair just like old times.

:-)

Cheers!

Flic x

Felicity Babbington-Smythe
Senior Talent Liaison Officer, NAFTA
Direct line: 0207 123 7896

on 27 July 2009, at 16:17, Zippy wrote:

Dear Felicity

Thank you for emailing me the ceremony details and running order. Everything seems to be in order. I'm sure it will be a night to remember. I do have one query – what is the dressing room situation?

Best wishes

Z

Zippy
CEO, The Zippy Foundation & ZPY Property Inc
30 St Mary Axe, London

Of course, Zippy and George had been forced to endure each other's company occasionally over the previous few years, but neither of them had set eyes on Bungle. Waiting in stony silence at the stage door, Zippy and George watched the bear jump off the No 29 bus, but he seemed flustered and could barely sustain eye contact when he puffed up to meet them.

As they made their way to the backstage holding area, Ant & Dec, red-faced and out of breath, ran up to meet them.

'Hi guys! We heard you were in the building and just couldn't let tonight go without saying hello,' enthused Dec. 'We are such huge fans.'

'Why thank you, erm, Dec? That's very kind,' said Zippy.

'You were the ones that made us want to go into telly in the first place,' explained Ant. 'I even wrote in for your autographs.'

'Oh I used to love getting my fanmail,' giggled George. 'Do you know what I used to do? It sounds silly now but I used to dab my signed photos with perfume. Now which one did I use? I can't remember…'

'Oscar de la Renta,' replied Ant, proudly. 'I've worn it ever since,' he added and held up a cuff-linked wrist for George to sniff.

'Oh Anthony, I am touched, I truly am,' said George. 'Now I really do feel like I have passed on the torch.'

Zippy rolled his eyeballs and looked to Dec for support. But Dec seemed equally enthralled by this and high-fived Ant, before giving him an excited hug: 'You have no idea how much meeting you both means to us.'

'Flippin nora,' thought Zippy. 'A double act that actually likes each other? Next you'll be telling me that Milli Vanilli had a five-octave vocal range…'

Typically, Bungle missed this encounter as he was in the Gents splashing cold water under his armpits.

After insisting on having their photos taken with their idols, Ant and Dec were called away to present the Best Cartoon award. Just then, Soo from *The Sooty Show* hurried by clutching at her ballgown. 'Hello, you two troublemakers, I haven't seen you for years!' she exclaimed as she stopped to air-kiss them. 'I must say you are both looking very well. Suspiciously well,' she said, her panda eyes darting from one to the other. 'In fact you don't look any different. Had any work done, Georgie-Porgie?'

'No, Soo-Soo darling, you know I don't believe in it. I'm just very lucky to have splendid genes, plus I eat healthily and drink oodles of lovely Evian.'

'Botoxed your brains out, more likely,' muttered Zippy.

'Anyway, boys, I must dash. I've just had a rather embarrassing

> 'Flippin nora,' thought Zippy. 'A double act that actually likes each other? Next you'll be telling me that Milli Vanilli had a five-octave vocal range'

wardrobe malfunction so need to change ASAP,' explained Soo. She turned to go and then smiled teasingly: 'You do know who is presenting your award, don't you?' They both shook their heads. 'Break a leg!' she shouted, laughing as she disappeared down the corridor.

With a sense of foreboding, Zippy grabbed the nearest flunky by the hoody and demanded to see the running-order. After speed-reading nearly forty pages of script Zippy and George were shocked to discover the Lifetime Achievement Award was to be presented by none other than their old flame, Sunshine – now the nation's sweetheart after surviving a very brave and public battle with temporary hair loss.

When Bungle reappeared from the Gents (Zippy was relieved to see no sign of regressive Toblerone abuse around his mouth) the trio were ushered into the wings. While stylist Mee-Ow and make-up artiste Brad flew to work on George, Zippy reached for a glass of vintage Vimto from the buffet table.

Bungle was pacing up and down as he planned what he was going to do next. His therapist Mike had told him that in order to move on from the past he would have to confront the co-stars that had made his life such a misery. So that's what he was going to do. As soon as they got on stage he was going to tell George and Zippy exactly what he thought of them. And then, at last, closure would be rightfully his...

When the stage manager gave them their two minute cue, there was a flurry of last minute make-up activity around George, Zippy straightened his bow-tie in a mirror and Bungle smoothed down the fur around his armpits which had started to curl with sweat again thanks to the borderline tropical temperatures in the wings.

They were ushered to the rear of the stage where a curtain

was going to be raised to reveal them standing side by side.

'Cue theme tune,' someone shouted and suddenly those old familiar words were filling the auditorium. 'Up above the streets and houses...' All three of them felt goosebumps. Before they knew it, they were being introduced: 'And now, ladies and gentlemen, boys and girls, together again for the first time in seventeen years – their rainbow is still flying high – yes, it's... George, Zippy and Bungle!'

'Why is George credited first?' Zippy thought fleetingly, while Bungle shrugged his shoulders, glumly accepting that he'd always got bottom billing. Their announcement was greeted by an astonished gasp from the unsuspecting crowd, which included Sophie Countess Of Wessex, Jude Law, Metal Mickey and a specially invited busload of *Rainbow* fans from Great Ormond Street children's hospital. The curtain flew up and Zippy, George and Bungle were revealed for all to see. As the threesome stepped forward into the blinding light the audience rose to its feet and roared their approval.

As the threeseome stepped forward into the blinding light the audience rose to its feet and roared their approval

After being handed the prestigious award by Sunshine – who gave both Zippy and George a typically kind-hearted smile – it was George who made it to the microphone first, determined to milk the moment for all it was worth.

'Hello everybody, oh, um, I don't know what to say. Oh dear, I'm filling up... and I said I wasn't going to cry!' he added, faltering for a moment and wafting his furry hand in front of his face in an attempt to calm himself down. Taking a deep breath he began again. 'I know I haven't had an orthodox career, and I've wanted more than anything to have your respect,' he explained, now getting into his stride. 'The first time I ever won an award

I didn't feel I had it. But this time, well, I feel I do and I can't deny the fact that you like me! Right now you really like me!'

The cheering audience lapped up such a heartfelt and original speech, whereas Zippy couldn't help but think he'd heard the whole thing somewhere before. Taking control of the situation before it slipped even further into a pit of mawkish sentimentality, Zippy prised the gleaming gong from George's vicelike grip and stepped up to the mike.

'Erm, I think what George is trying to say is that we are greatly honoured by this award and we'd like to thank everyone at the Academy for bestowing it upon us. Of course we couldn't accept without mentioning our esteemed colleague Geoffrey, who I do believe is here with us this evening. Stand up, Geoffrey, wherever you are!' Zippy held his hand to his eyes and peered into the clammy crowd. A brightly-dressed figure towards the back of the

auditorium near the Ladies stood up and waved and a ripple of applause could be heard from the audience. 'Thank you for all your support, Geoffrey, you have been a true friend and we couldn't have done it without you.' Zippy was warming to his theme. 'And I suppose, when one starts to think about it, that's what sums up *Rainbow* for all of us here on stage – friendship and support,' he said, looking at his former colleagues and forcing the most insincere smile George had ever witnessed.

'Friendship? Don't make me laugh!' cried Bungle, elbowing Zippy from the podium. This was it. This was payback time.

'You wouldn't know what friendship was if it came up and bit you on your bobbly backside. Maybe you'd like to tell me what was so friendly about tampering with the autocue to ensure my role was reduced on the show? That's not supportive, that's just being mean.'

By now a stunned hush had fallen around the auditorium.

Zippy gulped. 'How did you know about that?'

'He told me.' Bungle pointed at George who had hoped he was going to be left out of this rather ugly exchange.

'I'm sorry, Zippy, but Bungle was blaming himself for things that had gone wrong so I just happened to mention it.'

Zippy could feel the anger rising up inside him. 'It's not fair! I didn't do it, so mind your own beeswax, you blubbering blancmangehead. You really are a total waste of fur, aren't you?'

'Oh you're deigning to speak to me now, are you, Zippy?' retorted George, triumphantly. 'It's only taken you seventeen years.'

The audience were lapping up this unexpected turn of events. But, having watched the debacle unfold, Sunshine felt she couldn't keep a dignified silence any longer.

LEFT: Rows and recriminations; the ceremony descends into furry chaos

'Zippy, stop it,' she said, trying to calm the situation. 'There's no need to call Georgie names. I'm sure he didn't mean anything by it, he was just being honest,' For a brief moment, George and Sunshine caught each other's eyes and held their gaze. All these years later, after all the upset and heartache, there was undoubtedly still a connection between them.

Zippy was momentarily lost for words. 'Honest? Him? Sunshine, with respect, if I remember correctly he was doing the hokey cokey with Spit the Dog while you were at home preparing his Findus crispy pancakes and alphabetti spaghetti. Or had you somehow forgotten about that?' This resulted in muffled laughter from the audience.

Ignoring Zippy's comment, George stepped protectively in front of Sunshine. 'Zippy, as far as I'm concerned that's all in the past – rather like your failed acting career. I don't know why you are being so horrible. All I did was selflessly reach out to help a friend in need,' he added, sanctimoniously.

Bungle chuckled ruefully. But his eyes weren't smiling. 'You? A good friend?' he asked. 'Well now I have heard it all. Let's face it, George, you may surround yourself with the likes of Raymond and Gordon the Gopher, but all you ever do with them is talk about yourself. It's all about you, isn't it?'

George looked suitably miffed.

RIGHT: A moment of madness – Bungle dares to close Zippy's metal mouth fastener

'Oh Bungle! That's an awful thing to say,' he cried, his voice starting to quiver. 'As Barbra once sang so beautifully, people who need people are the luckiest people in the world and I have always considered myself to be one of those people.'

'But where were you when I needed you?' continued Bungle, exasperated. 'Is it any wonder I reached for the odd Curly Wurly or Panda Pop when I had to put up with you two squabbling and bickering on a daily basis? Oh and by the way, Sunshine, I'm going to tell you this because I think you're super and you have a right to know – it was Zippy who got you sacked from *Rainbow*.'

'Oops! Now I'm for it,' Zippy thought to himself, but decided to ride it out. 'Bungle, how could you insinuate such a thing...' he retorted. Zippy turned and looked pleadingly at Sunshine, but she just glared at him for a moment and then – thwack! – slapped him forcibly right across his metal mouth fastener. The audience took a sharp intake of breath and Sunshine tearfully fled the stage, clumps of recently re-grown hair tumbling to the ground behind her as she went.

By now the ceremony had turned into chaos. A runner was desperately trying to herd the threesome off stage but George was oblivious, boohooing like a baby and (in what he later described as 'a moment of madness') Bungle reached over and speedily slid Zippy's zip shut.

> **'That, Bungle Bonce is called assault and I have plenty of witnesses'**

Zippy's eyes looked as if they were going to pop out of their sockets. 'How dare you manhandle me!' he raged when he'd finally managed to unzip himself. 'That, Bungle Bonce, is called assault and I have plenty of witnesses,' he crowed, gesturing to the audience. Then he pulled his iPhone from his pocket and began to key in 999.

'Give that to me,' Bungle yelled. He lunged for the phone, but stumbled, tripped and ended up toppling onto a yelping Zippy which led to the pair rolling across the stage flapping their hands at each other and looking like a shag-piled version of Mickey Rourke in *The Wrestler*.

A shrill, child-like voice rang out from somewhere in the auditorium. 'Stop it! Stop it!' it cried. The audience craned their necks to see where the sound was coming from just as a follow-spot landed on a tiny blond-haired boy in a wheelchair who was slowly crawling his way down the centre aisle. There was a drip leading to his arm and it was clear he'd been crying.

'I thought you were all friends, but you were only pretending, weren't you?' accused the little boy, heartbroken. 'And I used to so love your stories, your brightly coloured fur and your funny voices...'

Despite not quite understanding how this very special night had gone so horribly wrong, George did his best to look poised – especially when he saw the number of camera-phones being held up around the stalls. Within minutes this rather embarrassing altercation was going to be all over YouTube. Meanwhile, Bungle wiped his brow. The scenario hadn't quite panned out how he'd planned and the heat on stage was roasting his brain as he tried to work out what to do next.

RIGHT: Stage fight; Zippy, Bungle and George grapple childishly for their award

Struggling for breath the teary boy grabbed his inhaler. 'I used to want to be just like you. Do you know what it's like to be a child who has a dream?'

George, Zippy and Bungle all hung their heads in shame and nodded. Unusually subdued, it was slowly starting to dawn on them that they had been seriously out of order. By this juncture, Geoffrey had made his way from the back of the auditorium and had lightly placed a comforting arm on the boy's shoulder: 'What's your name, sonny?' Geoffrey asked.

'My name is Oliver.'

'Hello Oliver. I'm Geoffrey. Now then, George, Bungle, Zip – I think you owe little Oliver here an apology. And frankly, I think it's about time you kissed and made up. Don't you?'

'I can't keep blaming other people for my mistakes. My name is Bungle and I'm an addict, but I would also like to be your friend'

A deathly quiet tumbleweed moment followed Geoffrey's request. Mortified, Zippy took a deep breath. He recognised a reality check when he saw one. They had all acted like spoilt children. And they were meant to be the ones setting the example. Now it was time to make amends. After apologising to Oliver he turned to his former co-stars. 'George and Bungle, I am sorry for my behaviour in the past. Oliver is right – we should've behaved better and I really hope we can put it all behind us and be friends again.'

Bungle could see Zippy was genuinely repentant and was surprised at how much that moved him. The hate he'd been carrying around with him all these years had been replaced by something else – empathy. This was just like being in H.A. he thought to himself.

'Thank you, Zippy. I accept your apology. It was unfair of

me to blame you for my problems. I can't keep blaming other people for my mistakes. My name is Bungle and I'm an addict, but I would also like to be your friend.'

Now, they both turned to look at a wobbly-lipped George, who had stepped forward and had placed their hands into his furry palm.

'I want to share a very special saying with everybody. A saying I have always related to, but until today perhaps never fully understood. "I've been to paradise but I've never been to me." It's from a poem by William Shakespeare. But do you know what, now I finally think I have been to me. My chums here have both just made me realise that it's not a luxury two week break at a Sandals resort in the Maldives or a five star Greek island cruise with your own personal manicurist and toast-butterer that matters. It's friendship that's important. I think we all just got a little distracted along the way,' he added, wiping a tear from his eye. 'Dear wheezy little Ollie, I'm so sorry. Haven't we all been silly sausages?'

All of a sudden Zippy could feel a wetness streaking down his face. Was he actually crying? He didn't want his mouth to rust over. The strange thing was, as the tear worked its way down to his zip, he noticed he seemed to be sobbing not from his eyes but from the top of his domelike forehead

All of a sudden Zippy could feel a wetness streaking down his face. Was he actually crying? He didn't want his mouth to rust over. The strange thing was, as the tear worked its way down to his zip, he noticed he seemed to be sobbing not from his eyes but from the top of his domelike forehead. George and Bungle looked strangely moist too. Drenched, in fact. It was then that Zippy looked up and saw a fountain of water spraying down at them from the rafters. It was the Royal Festival Hall's emergency sprinkler system which had automatically clicked into action thanks to the sauna-like heat that everyone on stage was having to endure.

Suddenly, there was an awe-stricken gasp from the audience. 'Look...' whispered Oliver, his whole face lighting up as he pointed upwards. Geoffrey, Zippy, George and Bungle followed the invalided child's gaze. Then they spotted it as well and their mouths dropped open. They couldn't believe what they were seeing. Through a combination of the bright theatre lights and the rain-like water that was falling between them, a giant, shining multicoloured archway had formed over the stage and was shimmering its way down into the stalls.

'It's...a rainbow,' squealed George, his eyes wide with amazement.

Uplifted and suddenly full of hope, an astonished Bungle could only quietly mouth, 'It's a sign.'

Then the audience began to whoop, thinking this was all a planned part of the evening's entertainment. But Zippy remained rooted to the spot, transfixed. Suddenly he was a little boy again. He was back in those dank cobbled backstreets of Macclechester, daydreaming about a better life, spurred on by the occasional colourful curve glimmering its way through the clouds.

He broke into a smile as wide as his zip would allow. 'Paint the whole world with a rainbow,' he mused, nodding with new-found knowledge. 'That's what it's all about...'

Acknowledgements

The author would like to thank: Emma Tait, Josh Ireland, Jim Lockwood, Claire Potter, Stuart Cooper, Filiz Tosun, Emma Norris, Rebecca Morris, Wendy Granditer, Andy Baker, Vicky Johnson, Lisa Marks, Kate Ashcroft, Sam Walker and Mark Horner. Special thanks to Jane Stead for her wisdom and words of wit.

Zippy, George and Bungle would like to thank: Geoffrey, Rod, Jane and Freddy, Raymond, Sunshine, Mike the Therapist, Jack Nicholson, Nelson Mandela and Susan Boyle. A very special thank you to Malcolm Lord, Ronnie Le Drew, Mark Mander and Roy Skelton, without whom we would not be where we are today.

Spit the Dog and Soo appear by kind permission of Bob Carolgees and Richard Cadell respectively. A huge thanks to both for their co-operation and sense of humour.

PICTURE CREDITS:
P18 © H. Armstrong Roberts/Corbis; P45 © Mike Maloney/Associated Newspapers/ Rex Features; P54 © Sullivan/Associated Newspapers/Rex Features; P55 © Rex Features; P62 *bottom right* © Rex Features *bottom left* © Richard Young/Rex Features; P70 © Press Association Images; P84 © L. J. van Houten/Rex Features; P87 © BBC Photo Library; P91 © Nils Jorgensen/Rex Features; P92 © Andre Csillag/Rex Features; P94 © ITV/Rex Features; P99 © BBC Photo Library; P106 © I.B.L./Rex Features; P 108 © The Sunday Times/Rex Features; P113 © Press Association Images; P137 © Press Association Images; P138 *bottom left* © Mark Richards/Daily Mail/Rex Features *bottom right* © Nils Jorgensen/Rex Features; P140 © Richard Young/Rex Features; P148 © ITV/Rex Features; P149 © Henry Lamb/BEI/ Rex Features; P150 *top* © BBC MOTION GALLERY *bottom* © BBC Photo Library; P151 © Ken McKay/Rex Features

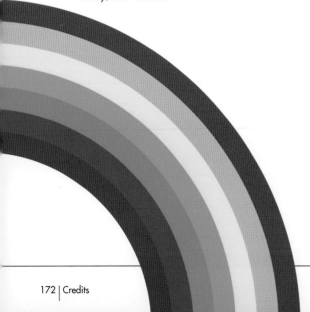